150 Years of Electric Horology

**With References to the Exhibit at the
1992 NAWCC National Convention
Chicago, IL July 1–4**

**Edited by
Elmer G. Crum
and
William F. Keller**

**NAWCC Chapter # 125
Midwest Electric Horology Group**

FOREWORD

Remember day-dreaming in grammar school as you waited for the bell signaling "go-home" time? Time dragged by as the minute hand of the strange clock on the wall jumped each minute rather than moving slowly like other clocks. How'd they do that? Or, the Western Union clock over the neighborhood soda fountain that had the little red light that always glowed a few seconds near the hour? What was that for? After all these years you can get the answers to these questions for these clocks which were but examples of the time pieces we turn to most in our everyday lives. Examples from the least known, and least studied, area of horology.

Today, such timepieces are the most abundant; by far the most popular in numbers purchased; the most varied in style, types, designs, sizes and prices; and one of the most popular items on earth. You can't look anywhere without seeing one or more! They are on your TV, VCR, electric range, radio, and car as well as in your kitchen and office. They are electric/battery clocks. In fact, you may even have one on your arm at this very minute, in a miniaturized version.

Oddly enough, this is not a new area of horology. The experimentation and design of these timepieces began over 150 years ago. In its history and development are included such names as Bulle, Bain, Jefferson, Eureka, Riefler, and Tiffany, not to mention such well-known names as Accutron, Hammond, Seth Thomas, Lux, Sessions, New Haven and many others.

The theme of the 1992 NAWCC National exhibit is "150 Years of Electric Timekeeping." The display items are from the number of afficionados throughout the country who specialize in this area of horology and the articles in this book have been written by experts from both the United States and England. This has been a massive undertaking and everyone associated with this "labor of love" is to be congratulated and complimented.

As interesting as the clocks in the display may be, they cannot compare with the involvement and enthusiasm their collectors display. They would be most pleased if everyone enjoyed this segment of our hobby as much as they. The entire group stands ready to share their expertise and secrets with us all. If you have an old (or new) electric/battery clock and need advice on its repair or history, you are passing up the best chance you will ever have for answers if you don't approach someone associated with this exhibit or book and ask some questions. That is one of the basic fundamentals of NAWCC — helping others with their collections.

We are indebted to all the people associated with the publication of this fine book and the preparation of the most interesting exhibit on which it is based. They have helped make us a little more aware of this oft overlooked area.

Tom LaRose, FNAWCC
Past-President

PREFACE

Anyone who undertakes the job of compiling and editing a volume such as this comes to realize that there is just not much information in print on the history of electric horology. True, there is considerable hearsay information passed about at chapter and other meetings, but verifying it is difficult. By the same token, most of the material in the literature deals with specific aspects of repair or design and is incomplete in so far as the people involved in the various firms, their early history or information on their products. Realizing all this, we still decided that someone had to attempt to assemble what data was available, fully aware that in so doing we would leave ourselves open to criticism. No matter what we and our contributors wrote, there would still be information that was not included.

Our original plan was for a little booklet, a catalog of the clocks in the exhibit, "150 Years of Electric Horology," which was to be the feature of the 1992 NAWCC National Convention in Chicago. That catalog, we felt, should contain photos of the clocks on display with descriptive legends and technical details being kept at a minimum. As we got farther along, however, we decided that were we to include short histories of the firms and the people whose products were in the exhibit it would make the book truly unique and a more useful reference. All this, we had hoped, could be contained within about 100 pages.

We soon realized, however, that there was a myriad of "electric" clock firms and that we would have a large percentage of them represented in our exhibit. What we had thought of as a little booklet could be a sizeable volume if we were to include photographs of most, if not all, of the several hundred clocks in the exhibit along with the histories we so desired to include. Accordingly, some compromises were required. First, we would only include photographs of representative clocks, not the entire exhibit. Second, we would make an effort to include a capsule history of all those firms for which we had or could find data, including some for which there was nothing exhibited. Third, we would not look at this as a local product, but would enlist the help of fellow NAWCC members who had information about specific firms. Fourth, we would try to cover but a small number of the many firms who made synchronous clocks because of space restraints, lack of validated information and the relatively short existence of many of the companies. Fifth, we would keep technical data to an absolute minimum — no electrical theory, no specifics on the various types of switches, etc. for those can be readily found in other sources. Sixth, we would have a short "Identifier Section" in the back of the book showing those clocks in the exhibit for which we could unearth little or no specific data. Finally, although we well realize the importance of those outside the United States in the development of electric horology, we would limit our coverage of these people in light of the number of fine works already available and emphasize American efforts.

What we have produced is, in our opinion, but a "primer" — a first book on a horologic subject that has long been neglected — an area that needs to be studied and about which more needs to be written. Although we have attempted to research many of the firms not covered here, we have run into far more dead ends than we had expected. We realize that this has resulted in a less than perfect volume, and we apologize for those omissions. We do, however, take pride in what is presented.

We trust that we, with the invaluable help of our many fine contributors, have been able to produce something of interest and value to all clock and watch enthusiasts, whether they be electrically-oriented collectors or not. If the volume serves to convert some of those who have not been interested in electrics before, we will be pleased, but that truly was not our goal. Our goal was to gather together, in what to our knowledge is the first such American effort, what information is available on those people and firms which were involved in the development of electric horology.

Although, to our minds, this work is something less than complete, it is the best that we could accomplish within our time restraints. We hope it will encourage others to take up the unfinished task by researching those companies on which there is no, or often sketchy, information at best and writing about them. Clearly, we plan to continue our efforts to learn more and, hopefully, to publish more. We would welcome any comments, criticism or information anyone perusing this volume might have.

EGC,WFK
May, 1992

ACKNOWLEDGMENTS

We often read an article or a book and wonder just where all the information therein came from, who really did the arduous tasks that made the final effort what it is. This venture would never have come to fruition without the help of many of our friends and acquaintances. These are people who were willing to give of their time and knowledge to supply or verify information we may have questioned. These were people who often went to their friends and secured answers to questions we had. They may or may not have written an article for which they knew they would get a byline, but all truly contributed much to this project. These were people without whom this work would not be what it is, for they truly gave of themselves without expecting anything but a "Thank You." The list is long and we sincerely trust that we have included everyone. If we have not, we apologize and we hope you will understand that the slight was truly unintended.

Charles K. Aked
West Drayton, England

John Anderson
Scotia, NY

Chris H. Bailey
Bristol, CT

Joe Bartels
Gardnersville, NV

Steven Berger
Algonquin, IL

Art Bjornestand
Westlake, CA

G. Harry Blair
Marlboro, NJ

Cathey & Tom Bober
Lansing, IL

Joe and Rusty Bourell
Chicago, IL

Bernard Bowman, Jr.
Columbus, OH

Don Brown
Thiensville, WI

Theodore Carbaugh
Waynesboro, PA

John Conklin
Elburn, IL

I.G. Cleator
Vancouver, B.C. Canada

Helen and Bob Core
Morgantown, WV

Pauline Crum
Skokie, IL

Jere DeVilbiss
Columbia, MO

Frank Dey
Los Angeles, CA

John Diehl
Terrace Park, OH

Lehr Diercks
Yellow Springs, OH

Eileen Doudna
Columbia, PA

Bernard Edwards, Sr.
Northbrook, IL

William Ellison
Grose Point Woods, MI

Jerry Fast
Belvidere, IL

George Feinstein
Flushing, NY

Mark Gulbrandson
St. Charles, IL

Larry Harnden, Jr.
Edmonds, WA

Don Henderickx
Maple Park, IL

Alfred Hoehn
Tucson, AZ

Homer Hollibaugh
Northlake, IL

C.M. Jauch
Louisville, MS

Frances Keller
Crystal Lake, IL

Howard Klein
Columbia, PA

Tom LaRose
Greensboro, NC

Steve Longo
St. Charles, IL

Tran Duy Ly
Fairfax, VA

Charles Middlebrooks
Naperville, IL

Leon O'Briant
Raleigh, NC

Brian Rogers
St. Louis, MO

Rene Rondeau
Corte Maders, CA

David N. Rooney
Boston, MA

Judith and Leonard Rubin
Chicago, IL

Harvey Schmidt
Flushing, NY

Harley Sheets
Morgantown, WV

Alan and Rita Shenton
Twickingham, England

William S. Stoddard
Lomax, IL

Martin Swetsky
Brooklyn, NY

George Theobald
San Francisco, CA

ACKNOWLEDGMENTS

Richard Tjarks
Howe, IN

Pat Tomes
Columbia, PA

Edward Voight
Manchester, VT

Susie Watson
Middlebury, CT

Hal Wehling
Cincinnati, OH

Ned Weymouth
Dayton, OH

James Whitacker
Granville, IL

Jeff Wood
Wilbraham, MA

Michelle Zoglauer
Marengo, IL

George & Linda Brusky
Chicago, IL

Steve Cunningham
Bedford, TX

John Darrow
Murrysville, PA

Dr. P.T.M. Doensen
Utrecht, The Netherlands

Dr. O.B. Frye
Phoenix, AZ

William G. Graves
Byron, MI

Marybeth Grisham
Dallas, TX

Burck E. Grosse
Palm Beach Gardens, FL

Brian Hegerly
Colorado Springs, CO

Doug Johnson
Crystal Lake, IL

James Johnson
Park Ridge, IL

Stan Kendzior
Chicago, IL

Ken Lesseberg
Montello, WI

David Miller
Hazelwood, MO

Lawrence A. Seymour
Bainbridge Island, WA

Martin Welch
Crystal Lake, IL

TABLE OF CONTENTS

Part III
IDENTIFIER SECTION

Part One
Historical Perspective

INTRODUCTION

To the uninitiated, an electric clock is one that is plugged into an electric outlet and is run by a synchronous motor. This is but one of the various types of electrics to aficionados of this area of horology. Their interests can include everything from the early battery-impulsed pendulum clocks, like those of Bain, to the atomic clocks of today. To many, synchronous clocks are of little interest since earlier electrics can be more intriguing, both mechanically and electrically. They feel that synchronous clocks are all quite similar mechanically and are really quite modern.

It was not until the 1920s that electric power systems began to have frequencies consistent enough to guarantee that synchronous clocks would operate efficiently and accurately. For some 80 years prior to that time, electric clocks were battery powered, either impulsing a pendulum, rewinding a spring or lifting a weight that used gravity as the power source. The chronology of developments in electricity and electric timekeeping that led to what we see today is covered elsewhere in this work, so we will not duplicate it here. Rather, we shall examine what went on in the early 1920s when there was a reluctance to buy battery-powered and synchronous clocks because of their poor reputation for reliability and how the market and marketing of clocks and watches, particularly electrics, has changed.

In the simplest terms, the earliest battery-powered clocks depended on an electromagnetic force to impulse a pendulum or balance wheel, using a toggle to close the electric circuit and give a "kick" when required. Although some of these clocks could be quite accurate, there were always problems with the contacts. Then, too, early batteries simply did not last as long as those made today. Now there are problems with people leaving *old* batteries in their clocks and watches.

In 1988, another battery-powered concept came to the fore with the introduction of the Self-Winding clock, which had its spring rewound hourly by an internal mechanism. Utilizing only a portion of the mainspring, these clocks were accurate timekeepers, and were widely used by railroads. A further advance permitted hourly corrections to be sent over telegraphic wires. This led to the development of the Western Union Time Service, characterized by the clocks found in their and many other offices until the late 1950s with a plate advertising "Naval Observatory Time."

A few years after the introduction of the Self-Winding clock, the Synchronome Clock System was developed in England and electric timekeeping truly came into its own. Still, these were battery-powered and used a pendulum as the regulating device. They were, however, to become the world standard for precision timekeeping for many years.

An interesting product of the mid-1920s came from the Sangamo Meter Company which used a motor that did not depend on a consistent electric current frequency and would operate over a range of currents from 80 to 125 volts AC. These clocks utilized a small spring, electrically wound and regulated by a platform watch escapement rather than a pendulum. Although well-conceived and well-engineered, the clocks suffered from having a relatively high price for

the times and from the appearance of more reasonably priced synchronous clocks a few years after their introduction.

Probably no person had more to do with the development of "mass market" electric timepieces than Henry Warren. After developing a synchronous motor which he hoped to use in clocks, he found it would not operate efficiently because of the variations in power frequencies previously mentioned. Accordingly, Warren solved his problem by developing a clock system to be used in power generating plants — a system that enabled plant operators to realize when the frequency was varying and to adjust their generators to insure the delivery of consistent power. Although he probably did not realize it at the time, Warren's master clocks also permitted the establishment of the power grids we know today, wherein plants outside an area can supply power to another area, when needed, since all are operating at 60 cycles.

In the early years of electric timekeeping, clocks and watches, whether electric or spring-driven, were sold by jewelry stores, probably because the jeweler/watchmaker

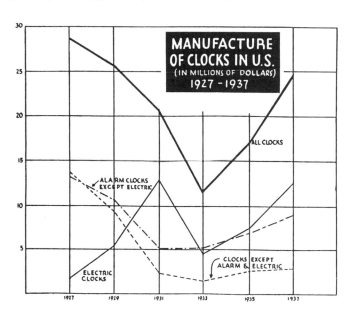

Graphic representation of clock manufacturing in the United States, 1927-1937. (*Jeweler's Circular Keystone,* November 1938.)

repaired them. This began to change in the late 1930s, however, as synchronous clocks were accepted as dependable, accurate timekeepers and generally did not require as frequent repairs as did spring-driven versions. Electric clocks sales grew from 87,333 in number in 1927 to 4,269,245 in 1937 according to the November, 1938 issue of *The Jewelers' Circular Keystone*. Spring-wound clocks, other than alarms, decreased in number during the same period, from 2,403,797 to 1,483,708. It is interesting that spring-driven alarm sales gained ever so slightly with 10,520,317 being sold in 1927 and 10,663,361 in 1937. Just why this happened, we can presume, was that workers who had to be to work on time still would not trust electric alarm clocks

INTRODUCTION

because of the outages and other vagaries of the power systems then experienced. Moreover, the article quoted above also suggested that there were those who just "like to hear a clock tick" when they retire.

It was during this period, also, that many traditional clock manufacturers began to market synchronous clocks, often with a notation such as "New Haven — Westinghouse," "Herschede — Telechron Powered" or something similar. Certain of the major spring- or weight-driven manufacturers, such as Herschede, also went to electrically wound

TEN-YEAR CLOCK PRODUCTION FIGURES
1927-1937

ELECTRIC CLOCKS

No.		Value
87,333	1927	$ 1,621,212
446,634	1929	5,193,243
3,797,499	1931	12,904,750
2,009,098	1933	4,821,884
2,500,148	1935	7,454,213
4,269,245	1937	12,651,716

ALARM CLOCKS, OTHER THAN ELECTRIC

No.		Value
10,520,317	1927	$13,120,007
9,462,293	1929	10,765,117
5,680,537	1931	5,111,068
6,698,778	1933	5,159,296
8,385,774	1935	6,906,409
10,663,361	1937	9,079,257

CLOCKS, OTHER THAN ALARM & ELECTRIC

No.		Value
2,403,797	1927	$13,967,131
2,386,284	1929	9,553,928
1,179,227	1931	2,375,067
943,235	1933	1,492,739
1,813,695	1935	2,754,411
1,483,708	1937	2,927,504

THE JEWELERS' CIRCULAR-KEYSTONE
for November, 1938

spring-driven clocks because, it has been stated, they did not feel synchronous clocks were reliable. As further evidence of this, when Herschede first marketed totally synchronous clocks they opted for a different name, "Revere," to keep from sullying the Herschede name with a product they evidently considered inferior.

As more and more reasonably priced electric clocks found their way into hardware, drug and other stores, jewelers' sales of small utilitarian electrics declined. Sales and repairs of simple spring-driven clocks which had long been an important part of their business, were also declining. Many essentially got out of the clock business, except for novelty clocks such as a Jefferson's Golden Hour, tall case and presentation models like the Atmos. Today, one sees few electric clocks in most jewelry stores, except for a few quartz desk clocks and other presentation models. Moreover, with the discounted prices being offered by other sales outlets, the jeweler often carries only those wrist watches that are of high-quality, whether they be quartz or spring-driven models, and many stores no longer have a watchmaker on premises, preferring to send repairs out. The advent of electric timekeeping has truly had an effect on the jewelry business even as it has affected all our lives.

William F. Keller, #12745

DEVELOPMENTS IN ELECTRIC HOROLOGY

In its 150-year history, electric horology has taken many wide and varied paths, some because of a lack of understanding of the very nature of electricity by early workers, some due to problems in the development of good electrical contacts, some due to a lack of understanding of horologic principles by those making the clocks and some partly due to the effects of two World Wars. Even so, the early efforts of Bain, Wheatstone, Ritchie, Hipp, Hope-Jones and others played a most significant role in the history of this aspect of horology, now in the electronic age with the development of the silent quartz-crystal-controlled watch.

Electric horology might be said to have begun in 1839-1840 when Alexander Bain patented the first clock system. His patent laid down all the principles that subsequent electric pendulum clock systems would use — even to this day. Bain's second patent evidenced the first really new thinking in clock propulsion, the impulsing of a pendulum solely by magnetic forces using electricity. Although the principles of these two patents have been stated and restated in almost all the patents issued to other electric horologists, Bain continues to be considered the "father of electric horology."

Some 12 years after Bain's initial work the next big advance was made when Matthias Hipp patented his Hipp toggle. During this period, more dependable storage batteries became a reality and our understanding of the fundamental principles of electricity greatly improved. Hipp devised a contact which depended on a small flag or toggle catching in a groove as the pendulum arc decreased. This caused the toggle to depress the switch contacts with greater force than had been achieved earlier and greatly increased the reliability of the system. Although the Hipp toggle has been modified and used in many other clocks — Murday, Rebesi, New York Standard Watch Company Electrics, Poole, Barr among others — the fundamentals remain the same.

Between Hipp's work in 1852 and 1888 there were few real improvements and no significant advances in this area of horology. Most of the concepts and ideas presented were but modifications of earlier work.

Chester Pond developed and patented the Self-Winding clock in 1888 and established a new company using that name. These clocks are said to have revolutionized the public and private timekeeping industries. They were probably the most dependable electrics ever made, a fact that is attested to by the numerous Self-Winding clocks that are still seen in Marts and collections. The Self-Winding Clock Company was also responsible for the most accurate and dependable time correction system, using telegraphic system wiring, which made hourly time correction possible. The correction was accomplished mechanically by sending a signal to each subscriber's clock which impulsed a set of coils causing a mechanical correction. These clocks were widely used by the growing railroad system and were seen in most Western Union offices.

The introduction of the Synchronome Clock System was the next significant development in electric horology. In 1895, Frank Hope-Jones developed a method of separating the impulsing and contact-making activities with the pendulum having little or no part in heavy work. Precision electric timekeeping had come of age! The Synchronome soon became the world's standard timekeeper and many continue to be used in observatories. The Synchronome was further improved in 1921 when W.H. Shortt coupled his hit-or-miss contact to the clock. This was the Shortt free pendulum which became the standard in precision pendulum clocks.

In considering the development of electric timekeeping we cannot overlook the very significant role of Henry Warren, who was primarily responsible for what many consider electric timekeeping. It was Warren who developed and patented the synchronous motor utilized in most electric clocks from 1919 until the advent of quartz timekeeping. Warren also developed a clock system that measured the frequency of alternating currents produced in generating plants so that consistent frequencies could become the rule, thus insuring the accuracy of his synchronous clocks. This development meant that extremely good timekeeping could be had by all, at a relatively low cost.

Finally, we reach the quartz phase of electric timekeeping which had its genesis in a clock developed by the Radio Corporation of America (RCA) in 1928. Utilizing 100 or so radio tubes and controlled by a quartz crystal, this clock was the size of a refrigerator — shades of early computers. The development of transistors during and after World War II permitted significant size reductions in the quartz movements and led to the development of the clocks and watches we know today. Further development of cesium and rubidium frequency standards permitted even more significant advances and has led to many new names in the industry; names such as Hewlett-Packard, Varain, Beckman and others.

No book on electric horology would be complete without a chronologic review of the advances in our knowledge of science and electricity, which formed the basis for all advances in electric timekeeping. Often we overlook the early research that paves the way for later work, and this might well be the case in this area. During the period from 1790 to 1840 many of the laws relating to how an electric current acts under controlled circumstances were postulated, laws which were, and still are, important in our study and review of this segment of horology. After Bain's 1840 patent and manufacture of a truly electromagnetic clock, there was a period of continuous development and application of electricity to timekeeping.

CHRONOLOGY

1790 - Galvani conducted his famous frog muscle experiment. The Galvanometer, which we know as a voltmeter, is named for him.

1800 - Alexander Volta made the first battery. The unit of electric pressure, the volt, is named for him.

1820 - Oersted demonstrated that an electric current would attract or deflect a compass needle evidencing the magnetic effect of the current.

DEVELOPMENTS

1820 - Ampere demonstrated that a coil of wire when energized became a temporary magnet.

1825 - Sturgeon constructed the first electromagnet with an iron core. He is also credited with the discovery of the polarity of an armature in 1836.

1825 - Ohm developed his theoretical law I=E/R, the basic formula for all electric measurements.

1830 - Zamboni constructed an electrostatic clock utilizing static electricity (but not too successfully).

1831 - Faraday discovered the principle of induction in a coil.

1832 - Henry discovered the principle of self-induction (back EMF, the current that causes contacts to pit and burn as they open)

1832 - Pixii constructed the first electromagnetic generator

1834 - Matthias Hipp constructed the Hipp toggle and switch, but did not put it to practical use until 1842. His invention has been rediscovered many times.

1836 - Daniell built the first battery based on the lead/acid principle.

1836 - Jacobi built the first motor based on electromagnetic principles.

1840 - Alexander Bain made and patented the first practical electromagnetic clock.

1847 - Foucault, best known for his Foucault pendulum, experimented with a synchronizer for balance wheel clocks based on electric principles. Some also credit him with developing the device known as the Hipp toggle.

1849 - Sheppard, who is best known for the Greenwich gate clock, was also the first man to use the weighted arm to impulse the pendulum.

1854 - Alexander Hall of Lloydsville, Ohio secured a patent for an electric clock, the first in the United States. Patent #11,723 featured an electromagnetically rocked verge.

1856 - Lois Breguet constructed a clock which was remotely rewound by an electric motor.

1860 - Hipp constructed his first practical electrically-driven clock.

1863 - Hipp, in conjunction with astronomer Hirsh, designed and constructed a system of time transmission for the Swiss Postal Service.

1880 - Pierre Curie discovered the principle of piezo electricity, the ability of a quartz crystal to oscillate when an electric current is applied.

1888 - Chester Pond patented the first commercially-successful electrically-operated clock rewound with a motor.

1895 - Hope-Jones developed the Synchronome clock system, the first high precision electric clock system.

1899 - Thury experimented with the first synchronous motor to operate clocks.

1903 - Sigmund Riefler was the first to use an electrically reset weight in an astronomical clock, setting the stage for controlled atmosphere regulation of clock rates.

1905 - Schlesser built the first clock using a photocell as a switch to drive impulsing coils in a clock.

1910 - Lee DeForest perfected the first three-element radio tube known as a triode, allowing small signal amplification.

1912 - The first radio time signals were transmitted from Eiffel Tower.

1913 - The Stern-Gerlach experiments lead to the development quantum mechanics, knowledge important to the development of the atomic clock.

1917 - Henry Warren constructed the first practical synchronous motor clock.

1918 - Warren developed the first clock that could be used to control the frequency of A.C. generators, thereby permitting consistent frequencies, and accurate time, to all those on the service grid.

1921 - W. Shortt invented and patented with Hope-Jones the system known as The Shortt Free Pendulum, which was to become the world standard of precision timekeeping for the next 25 years.

1923 - Stern was named head of Physical Chemistry at the University of Hamburg. During the following 10 years, he and his students developed the basic principles and techniques used in today's atomic beam frequency standards.

1928 - RCA built the first quartz crystal controlled high precision clock based on a vacuum tube.

1932 - O. Frisch and E. Segre experimented with potassium as a frequency standard.

1938 - I. Rabi at Columbia University developed the theory of magnetic resonance.

1939 - 1944 was a period of little research in electric horology because many of the researchers were pressed into related war work. That research, however, led to rapid post-war advances in the field of atomic frequency standards.

1949 - The first experiments with optical pumping were conducted by Prof. F. Bitter at M.I.T. A year later he and Brossel made practical application of Bitter's findings in the establishment of rubidium frequency standards.

1952 - Elgin builds a laboratory model of a grade 725 electric watch.

1954 - IBM offers the first commercially available clock that is corrected by signals from WWV.

1955 - Bell Telephone Laboratories produces the first transistors leading the way to miniaturization of electronics.

1958 - Hamilton Watch Company introduces the first electric watch, the 500 model.

1958 - Rubidium and cesium frequency standards were established by A. Bloom and W. Bell of Varain, and M. Arditi and T. Carver of the ITT labs. Varian used the first optical detectors.

1960 - Ramsey, Goldberg and Keppner of Harvard developed the hydrogen maser.

1961 - Bulova Watch Company introduced the first electronically controlled watch — model 218 (and it hummed).

1962 - Thallium frequency standards were established by J. Bonanomi of Neuchatel Observatory in Switzerland.

1967 - The rubidium gas frequency standard is produced by Varian in conjunction with Hewlett-Packard. It was accurate to 3-10'10.

1967 - Texas Instruments introduced the first light-emitting diode (LED) watches.

1969 - The first cesium frequency standards are introduced and they soon become the universal time standard.

1971 - The General Conference of Weights and Measures adopts the Atomic Time Scale.

1972 - The International Atomic Time Scale is the official time measure of most countries worldwide.

1975 - The first liquid crystal display (LCD) watches appear, mostly from Japan.

1980 - The first multi-purpose (time, calculator, etc.) watches appear.

1992 - Greater accuracy for all timekeeping devices is assured in the future.

NOTE - This chronology of milestone dates is not all-inclusive, nor written in stone. The data from which it was prepared is not even so. Its purpose is to provide readers with a point of reference from which they can continue their own research into the history of electric development and its application to modern time-determining standards. Hopefully, this will lead to an improved understanding of the hardware associated with the accuracy we are inclined to take for granted today.

Elmer G. Crum, FNAWCC #33463

Part Two
Catalog of Exhibit

The American Clock Company

The American Clock Company of Chicago traces its origins to The Automatic Electric Clock Company, incorporated in Kansas City in 1897, and the United States Pneumatic Clock Company of Chicago, which Automatic absorbed in 1901. At that time, the two merged firms were renamed American Clock and reorganized with a capital of $1,000,000.

Although organized in Kansas City, the original firm listed its address as 231 S. Canal in Chicago and listed W.C. Bryan of that city as its General Manager. The first patent relating to the company was issued in September, 1898 to Fred Getty of Chicago who assigned it to Automatic. From all appearances, most, if not all, of the clocks manufactured were patterned after this patent.

The turn of the century seemed to be a true turning point for the original firm. They had a large exhibit of their clocks at the Paris Exposition, taking Gold Medals for timekeeping excellence and artistic case design; they completed new facilities at 385 S. Wabash and they offered a wide range of clocks, from mantle to tall case, ranging in price from $20 to $60. In that same year, C.J.M. Porter was appointed General Manager and several changes were made in their sales staff.

Within the next year came the amalgamation with the United States Pneumatic, manufacturers of the Hahl Pneumatic Clock System, and the reorganization into the American Clock Co., which continued to make the pneumatic system under the Hahl name for a number of years. Officers of the new firm included men from a number of prominent Chicago firms: a Vice-President from the Pullman Car Co., one from Murphy Varnish, another from Pullman, and the President of the Commercial National Bank. The new firm exhibited at the Pan American Exhibit in Buffalo, where it aggressively promoted its Hahl pneumatic synchronous system, its electric clocks, regulators, and electric time stamps.

During the period 1902-1905 the firm was assigned four patents, three from Fred Getty and another from Harry W. Pidgeon. Evidently, the firm had been incorporated in New Jersey, even though it operated from Chicago, since all the assignments show that address for the company. There is no evidence that any clocks were every produced outside the Chicago facilities or of manufacturing plants elsewhere.

The clocks are easily identified by their unusual stick type of movement configuration. They use only three wheels with two weighted arms on the right side and a dead-beat anchor escapement, often with jeweled pallets. They are designed to run on two #6 dry cells and are some of the more cherished pieces in many electric clock collections.

Suggested Reading

1. Wood, Stacy B.C., Jr., 1983: The American Clock Co., Chicago, IL, *NAWCC Bulletin*, XXV:76-80.

2. Hagans, Orville R., (ed), 1979: *The Best of J.E. Coleman: Clockmaker*, Denver, CO, American Watchmakers Institute Press, pp. 382, 428.

3. Goodrich, W.L., 1905: *The Modern Clock*, Chicago, IL, Hazlitt and Walker, Publishers, pp. 393-399.

4. Anonymous, 1980: American Clock Company: Advertising Brochure, *The Journal of Electrical Horology*, February

Elmer G. Crum, FNAWCC, #33463

Cherry-cased regular model. *Left,* front view of clock. *Right,* photo of "stick" type movement with two weights seen on the right side of the in-line plates.

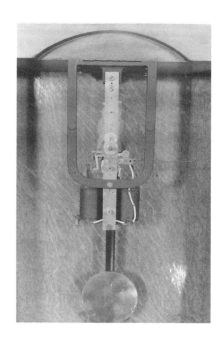

Mahogany Sheraton cased mantle model.

Oak-cased regulator model. *Left*, front view of clock. *Right*, unusual, for American clock rotary movement. It may be a prototype since there is no serial number on the movement.

Crystal regulator model with mercury pendulum and round mantle movement.

Mission mantle model, mahogany cased. *Left*, front view of clock. *Right*, rear view with case door open to show the mantle clock movement with jeweled escapement, mercury pendulum and unusual rating adjustment.

Mahogany mantle model with typical mantle movement.

ATO

Two of the most popular and practical battery electric clocks of the early 20th century were designed by Marius Lavet while working for Favre Bulle. The first design used by Bulle involved a stationary magnet and a moving coil. The second design was adopted by the firm (ATO) of Leon Hatot. It involved a stationary coil and a swinging magnet, an idea Charles Féry used in 1908. The ATO clock was first marketed in 1923 and continued to be made into the 1950's. The clocks sold well in the European market, but few found their way to the United States.

Movements were made in two sizes, a large model with a half-second beat and a 25 cm (10 in) pendulum and a smaller model with a quarter-second beat and a 6 cm (2 3/8 in) pendulum. The movements were actually quite small, with circular plates only about 3 cm (approx. 1 3/16 in) in diameter. The larger model was fitted with a sweep second hand, and could be supplied with contacts for operating remote dials using half-minute impulsing. These larger models had Invar pendulum rods, were very accurate and were widely used by the French railroad system.

ATO produced a wide variety of cases for the smaller movement. They began, in 1924, with only four cases, but by 1929, had broadened the line to over 50 models. Many of the models for residential use were cased in marble and Lalique glass in addition to bakelite and wood cases. From 1928 to 1932 ATO clocks were made under license by the Hamburg American Clock Company and following the HAC takeover, by Junghans which continued production until 1962.

The contact arrangement on the large movement is unique in that it actually impulses the pendulum in the center of the arc of the swing, something mechanical clockmakers were never able to achieve. The design also incorporated a damping system using a second dummy coil, basically a one-turn coil that set up eddy currents in opposition to the magnetic polarity thus "damping" the action of the pendulum. When set up properly, these clocks will operate within a second per day accuracy.

Heavy marble mantle model. *Upper,* front view. *Lower,* rear view showing the movement.

Mini-desk model. *Upper,* front view. *Lower,* rear view showing 180-beat movement.

In 1953, when Hatot was 70 years old, he and Marius Lavet secured a patent for the use of transistors in the switching of the ATO clock. The first electrically driven transistorized clocks were made, under license, by Kieninger and Obergfell (Kundo) in 1954. These clocks were of horologic significance because this was the first use of transistors in a clock for general public use. Basically, the pendulum on these clocks was impulsed in a manner quite similar to that of their original long pendulum clocks except for the inclusion of a "switching" or "sensing" coil. The transistors eliminated the ever-present problem of contact sparking and dirt, greatly improving the reliability of the clocks.

It is of interest that Hatot and Lavet, in their original 1953 patent for transistor switching, mentioned the possibility of producing a transistor-switched balance wheel clock. Some eight years later this became a reality with the production of the ATO-MAT movement which was made as a replacement movement by Kienzle and others, some with floating balances. These were widely used as replacement movements until the advent of quartz controlled replacements.

Among the American firms licensed to make ATO movements were Seth Thomas, Bulova and Elgin. Clocks with these movements can generally be easily recognized. All ATO models are quite collectable and are good timekeepers.

Suggested Reading

1. Hanson, E., 1991: The electric clocks of Leon Hatot, *Clocks,* 14:24-29.

2. Hope-Jones, Frank, 1940: *Electrical Timekeeping,* London, England, N.A.G. Press.

3. Wilding, John, 1978: *How to Make a Simple Battery Clock,* Ashford, Kent, England, Brant Wright Associates, Ltd.

4. Anonymous, 1988; ATO Junghas Transistorized clocks, *The Journal of Electrical Timekeeping,* December.

Elmer G. Crum, FNAWCC, #33463

ATOMIC CLOCKS

The companies now responsible for providing the equipment for timing the world are Hewlett Packard, Varain, Beckman, RCA, Efratom, Tracor and others whose names seem to say nothing about clocks — but, let's look further.

The age of electronic time can be said to have begun in 1880 with Pierre Curie's discovery of piezoelectricity and the quartz crystal. Originally, his discovery was not applied to the, then young, science of electricity, but to the measurement of radioactivity by a device known as the piezoelectric quartz electrometer. Until 1920, very little application of the quartz crystal to the art of timekeeping was made. With the advent of the radio and the vacuum tube, however, experimentation with quartz ultimately led to its application to the first frequency standards which were controlled by a quartz crystal.

The first quartz crystal clock, so to speak, was constructed at the Bell Laboratories in New York City in 1928 by J.W. Horton and W.A. Morrison. Two years later, D.W. Dye and L. Essen working at the National Physical Laboratory in Teddington, England also constructed a quartz controlled clock.

The scope of this work precludes a technical explanation of the quartz crystal oscillator, the ammonia clock, the rubidium gas oscillator, the cesium oscillator and the hydrogen maser. All except the ammonia clock are in current use as frequency standards. Should the reader be interested in learning about their technical workings, the Suggested Readings at the end of this article contain in-depth explanations.

The first "atomic clock" was placed in operation during the years 1948-1949 by the National Bureau of Standards, Boulder, Colorado. The development and use of this ammonia clock culminated 15 years of research.

The use of a cesium oscillator as the calibration standard by the National Bureau of Standards in 1958 was the next step in the use and development of atomic clocks. Similar uses by the National Physics Laboratory in England in conjunction with the U.S. Naval Observatory were reported as early as 1955.

The Hewlett-Packard Company was established in 1939 in Palo Alto, California, to build high quality and precision test equipment for the growing electronics industry. Most of the war years, however, were spent in the production of war goods. By 1961, the firm had become a leader in the time-measurement field, employing over 2,800 people, most of them highly-skilled electronics engineers. In 1963, they performed their "flying clock" experiment using Varain cesium frequency standards. This experiment compared the four cesium frequency standards in use at the time by flying a clock to various locations around the world to make on-site comparisons, a feat unattainable earlier. It was demonstrated that, at that time, the clocks were all within 4×10^{-12} seconds of agreement.

The use of cesium and rubidium standards permitted more accurate time-keeping, not only for keeping world time per se, but also by the military, television, industry, land and sea navigation and our space efforts. All needed the timing accuracy of this equipment in order to succeed.

The cost of an early rubidium or cesium frequency standard was near $50,000, not including the clock dividers for the display of time. A complete set-up in the 1960-1970s could cost as much as $200,000 for a U.S. Coast Guard LORAN installation. The equipment in the exhibit is traceable to the Coast Guard facility in Milwaukee, Wisconsin where it was used for about five years before being replaced by a newer, more accurate system in 1971. Costs of such gear have dropped considerably as more manufacturers have entered the field and better materials were developed. The equipment is now about one-third the original size and is quite portable.

The reason for the accuracy of these clocks can be better understood when one realizes the cesium has attained a short-term accuracy of 3×10^{-13} second — that is 0.00000000000003 second!

It should be mentioned that "atomic clocks" is a misnomer, for no harmful alpha, beta or gamma radiation is involved — contrary to what many people think. The radiation emitted by cesium

Two Hewlett Packard clock dividers, one driven by a quartz crystal oscillator and the other by a rubidium oscillator. Circa 1960. This clock was originally in the Coast Guard station in Milwaukee, Wisconsin and has been recased.

and rubidium is photon radiation and poses no atomic threat.

Suggested Reading

1. Anonymous, *1974: Time and Frequency: Theory and Fundamentals,* (BS Monograph 140), Washington, DC, U.S. Department of Commerce.

2. Rawlings, A.L., 1974: *The Science of Clocks and Watches'* 2nd ed.,

3. Hewlett-Packard 1961 catalog.

4. Jespersen, J., & Fitz-Randolph, J., 1977: *From Sundials to Atomic Clocks,* (NBS Monograph 155), Washington, DC, U.S. Government Printing Office.

5. Anonymous, 1990: *Time and Frequency Users Manual,* rev. ed., (NIST Special Publication 559), Washington, DC, U.S. Government Printing Office.

Elmer G. Crum, FNAWCC, #33463

ALEXANDER BAIN

Alexander Bain remains one of the most neglected figures of applied technology in nineteenth century Britain. Twentieth century writers on the history and principles of electric clocks, such as Frank Hope-Jones, were biased against Bain, a tradition going back to the 1850's when Sir Edmund Beckett denounced electric clocks saying that they were unable to work for any extended period of time. As a result, Alexander Bain's work came to be regarded as pioneering, but of little importance in the development of electric timekeeping and telegraphy. More modern research and writing has resulted in a change of opinion regarding his contributions.

Born near the village of Watten, Caithness, Scotland in 1810, Bain was apprenticed to a watchmaker in Wick. Regarded as a day-dreamer, he spent over five years as an apprentice in Wick. His attendance at a seminar in the nearby town of Thurso on the subject of "Heat, Light and Electricity" proved to be the catalyst for breaking his apprenticeship and moving to Edinburgh. Bain's activities in Thurso are obscure, but he seems to have completed his apprenticeship since, in 1837 he obtained employment as a journeyman clockmaker in Clerkenwell, London, then the mecca of all those interested in the art of clockmaking. He took advantage of his new proximity to the cultural center of London and attended the many public educational lectures, then popular, at such places as the Adelaide Gallery and the Polytechnic Institute.

Writing much later about this period of his life, he mentions his pleasure at viewing "the wonderful electro-magnetic apparatus in action at these places," and considering how these could be applied to useful purposes, — "The application of this mysterious power to the mechanism of his own business (clockwork) was naturally the first to suggest itself;..." Less than a year after his arrival in London, in early 1838 to be precise, he confided to his friend, Charles McDowall, how he intended to apply electricity to clockwork. By June 1840 he had advanced in his work to the point that he was able to invite McDowall to a demonstration of his newly invented Centrifugal Clock and an electric clock.

Early, circa 1856, Alexander Bain wall clock. (Photo courtesy of the Science Museum, London, England)

Shortly afterwards, Bain sought financial backing to allow him to produce commercial models. As is true in the case of many inventions, the world was not waiting or anxious for the fruits of his labor. Fate conspired to bring him to a meeting with Charles Wheatstone, soon to be acclaimed as the "inventor" of the telegraph. Their relationship began cordially enough, with Wheatstone paying Bain the sum of 5 pounds for the models of his electric clock and printing telegraph and offering 150 pounds for an improved version of the electric printing telegraph. In the

weeks that followed, however, Wheatstone deceitfully had his workman, John Lamb, construct an electric clock to Bain's design. This, and efforts to pass the clock off as Wheatstone's own invention, caused a bitter and prolonged quarrel between the two men, the account far too lengthy to be detailed here.

Meanwhile, Alexander Bain had applied for an all-embracing patent for electricity applied to clockwork which was granted in 1841. His first electric clock was a weight-driven pendulum clock fitted with electric contacts operated by the pendulum or train. The pulses of the electric current could be used to operate "companion" clocks through a circuit of copper wires. Bain mentions that he envisioned the universal distribution of time signals throughout Britain from a single accurate master clock. His first true electric clock, i.e., one in which the pendulum was impulsed directly by electric currents, did not appear until circa 1843 and was not a practical proposition until his later invention of solenoid impulsion for pendulum.

Bain returned to Edinburgh in 1844 and set up business as an "Electric Clock and Telegraph Maker." He linked the cities of Edinburgh and Glasgow by a single conductor telegraph line in 1846 and demonstrated time transmission by means of an electrically driven master pendulum clock in Edinburgh driving a slave pendulum clock in Glasgow in sympathy, using the earth as the return part of the circuit.

There was a quarrel between Bain and Wheatstone when Wheatstone and his partner sought Parliamentary approval for a wayleave on behalf of their Electric Telegraph Company. Bain lodged an objection to this and eventually the House of Lords ruled in his favor. (The report of the testimony and technical arguments in this case cover many pages). Bain was awarded 7,500 pounds, plus having the satisfaction of knowing that the Electric Telegraph Company would manufacture electric clocks to his system and provide the working capital. His name would appear on the dial of each clock as the patentee and he would receive half of the working profits from the sales of

Bain mantle clock inscribed "Patent Electric Clock" beneath the XII, and "A. Bain, Inventit, NO. 185" above the VI. *Left*, front view. *Center*, side view of movement showing the relatively simple gearing and superior workmanship. *Right*, dial and works removed to show the sliding contact arrangement and the pendulum.

such clocks. In return, Bain had to recognize the validity of Wheatstone and Cooke's patents. Wheatstone then resigned as a company Director.

This award enabled Bain to return to London where he set up a small factory and showroom for electric clocks at 43 Bond St. He produced a variety of electric clocks which evidently tied up a large portion of his capital. It cannot have been a very lucrative venture because he sold only forty clocks up to 1849 and the price of a master clock began at only twelve guineas, slightly more than 12 pounds.

Bain's later years are somewhat difficult to follow. He seems to have made several trips to America to install his telegraph systems and here he came in conflict with Samuel Morse. The litigation to determine priorities proved very costly to Bain (the author believes he would have been successful in a British court). He returned to England in 1860 absolutely penniless, to spend his last years as a sad and disillusioned man. He was befriended by Lord Kelvin who used his influence to persuade Prime Minister William Gladstone to grant Bain a state pension of 80 pounds per annum. However, Bain became so itinerant that no one knew where to find him to pay his pension. He died in Kirkintilloch in January 1877 and is buried in Old Aisle Cemetery, where his monument is maintained in perpetuity by the Coun-

cil. Over a century later his genius is receiving long-delayed recognition.

Suggested Reading

1. Bain, Alexander, 1852: *A Short History of Electric Clocks...*, London, Chapman And Hall. (Reprinted in 1973 by Turner and Devereux, London).

2. Aked, Charles K., 1977: *A Conspectus of Electrical Timekeeping*, Ticehurst, Sussex, England, The Antiquarian Horological Society.

3. Aked, Charles K., 1977: *Electrifying Time*, Ticehurst, Sussex, England, The Antiquarian Horological Society.

Charles K. Aked, FNAWCC, #29401

BANGOR ELECTRIC CLOCK COMPANY

Located in Bangor, Maine, the Bangor Electric Clock Co. is yet another of those on which the little that has been published is widely scattered and often rather abstruse. We are told that Bangor clocks were of an intricate design and the only patent to be found relating to them was issued to a Walter J. Dudley who seems to have lived, at one time or another, in Everett, Maine, Somerville, Maine, Bangor, Maine and possibly even Waltham, Massachusetts.

Even with the little published on Bangor, Dudley's name comes up rather frequently in connection with a number of companies and from this we can glean something about the Maine operation. Walter J. Dudley held a number of patents relating to electric clocks and his first two, #447,105 and #465,655 were issued in 1891. A clock showing these patent dates and listed as being an "Independent Electric Clock," possibly of his own manufacture, was sold at auction in North Falmouth, MA in 1958. It was in the same year as his previous patents, 1891, that Dudley and Walter K. Menns, a British subject and an incorporator of the Waltham Electric Clock Company, secured yet another patent for an electric clock. This would seem to be the patent on the mechanism used in the Waltham firm's products.

In 1900, while residing in Somerville, Dudley secured another patent(#648, 487) and about three years later, while living in Bangor and associated with the Bangor firm, he is said to have secured another.

As one can see from the foregoing, Dudley was involved in a number of electric clock ventures without ever seeming to have hit the jackpot. His career could be an interesting and rewarding research project.

Suggested Reading

1. Bemis, Dr. Anthony, (ed), 1958: The Answer Box, Sale in Massachusetts, *NAWCC Bulletin*, VIII:356.

2. Feldman, Martin C., 1981: An Intricate Bangor Electric, *NAWCC Bulletin*, XXIII:499.

William F. Keller, #12745

BLODGETT BROS. & CO.

Blodgett Bros. & Co. was an early electric business started in Boston, Massachusetts by two brothers, George and Aaron Blodgett, in 1879. They were manufacturers of, and dealers in, a variety of electrical goods including bells, annunciators, electric batteries, and electric signal clocks for ringing bells at railroad stations. Both men were graduates of the Massachusetts Institute of Technology.

In the 1890s, Blodgett used Standard Electric Time Company movements to produce a master clock bearing their name and a Standard Electric #2 movement to drive their program machine. By 1894, they had installed a self-winding electric master clock and 23 secondary clocks in the Somerville, Massachusetts High School. The program to ring the bells was on a punched paper tape. Over 19 systems were installed in various schools, primarily in Eastern Massachusetts, by 1897. Considerable business came from the Boston Public School System, and by 1910 Blodgett had their system in at least 34 Boston schools, including large high school buildings such as Dorchester High, West Roxbury High, South Boston High and Brighton High.

Sometime around 1900, the company began to use the "F" movement made

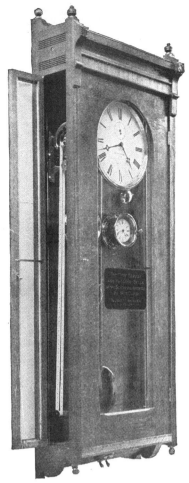

Advertising illustration of a Blodgett "signal" clock.

by the Self-Winding Clock Company of New York in their master clocks. Subsequently, they began to manufacture their own master clock movements based on a patent granted Aaron Blodgett in 1909. These movements wound the main spring once each hour and were powered by two dry cells.

George Blodgett left the company to pursue other interests in 1902, and the firm was reorganized as the Blodgett Clock Company with Aaron as President. Then, in 1908, the company was sold to the Industrial Instrument Company of Foxborough, Massachusetts with Aaron Blodgett continuing to operate the business at 141 Franklin Street in Boston. Business fell off dramatically by 1911 and the firm was again sold, this time to Mr. George Riggs of Standard Electric Time. The business continued to operate as the Blodgett Clock Company until 1914 when the Boston factory was closed and the firm went out of business.

At the time of this writing in 1992, there are no complete Blodgett systems known to be operating in the United States. It is believed that the company made about 400 master clocks between 1894 and 1913.

David N. Rooney, #74456

THE BULLE CLOCK

Maurice Phillipe Favre-Bulle, the patentee of the Bulle clock, holds a total of fifteen British patents. The initial one (#161,650) applied for on January 9, 1920 bears the name of Mme. Veuve Marcel-Andre-Moulin nee Berthe-Marie Marguerite Chenard, the widow of Marcel-Andre Moulin as co-patentee. The registered address of both parties was 17 rue Gambetta Boulogne sur Seine, Paris, France.

Professor Marcel Moulin, born November 1, 1881 at Louviers, France, studied at Lycie d'Erreux and Lycie Voltaire. After a year's military service he became a reserve officer, obtaining his science degree in 1904 and his Doctorate in Science in 1910. He became a Lecturer in Chronometry at the Faculty of Science Bensacon and in 1910 was named Professor and Director of the

Institute where he published treatises in the Bulletin de l'Observatoire de Besancon and La France Horologere.

By 1912 Moulin had developed the system of using a solenoid with a three-pole tungsten magnet and by 1914 he used, for the first time, the consequent pole magnet in the construction of an electric clock — a concept little used before 1920. Meanwhile, Favre-Bulle concentrated on developing the mechanical aspects of the clock. Favre-Bulle and Moulin combined efforts and produced a prototype clock but further work on the project was interrupted by the onset of World War I.

As a reserve officer, M. Moulin was called into service in the 204th Infantry Regiment, serving in the Battle of Marne where he was killed on Septem-

ber 6, 1914 while leading his company in an attack on enemy trenches.

Maurice Phillipe Favre-Bulle, called Favre Heinrich, was born at Besancon and was a member of an old family of clockmakers. He studied at l'Ecole d'Horlogerie de Besancon from 1885-1888 before joining his brother in taking over the running of the Favre-Heinrich factory that his father had founded. After the death of his brother, Maurice assumed full responsibility for the factory and concentrated on precision work. He received many awards in International Expositions and became a member of the Commission of Examiners in addition to being appointed Clockmaker to the Navy. He founded the trade journal *La France Horlogere* in 1901, but relinquished his duties in 1907 when he went to Paris to

THE BULLE CLOCK

continue his research in technical horology.

The Legion d'Honeur was awarded him in 1910. During the period from 1914-1918 (World War I) he worked at the Engineering Laboratories of the Faculty of Sciences of Paris where he developed numerous items for military use: aviator's watches, revolution counters, meters, and wireless telegraphy and telephony devices. He also studied possible methods of synchronizing the vibrating blade following the work of Hipp on the vibrating spring escapement used in chronoscopes and chronographs intended for measuring small intervals of time.

At the end of the war (1918), Favre-Bulle joined with Marius Lavet to found La Societe Bulle et Cie, where prototype electric clocks were made and in 1920 founded Compagnee Generale des Appareils Horo-Electrique for the commercial development of electric clocks. It is estimated that some 300,000 clocks were made during their production run from 1920 to 1952. Most of the clocks appear to use the contact system outlined in Bulle's patent of 1920. Although cased in some 100 different cases, it is interesting that those in tall glass domes on a wooden base seem to be most commonly found in NAWCC Marts.

Over the years, the movements remained relatively unchanged although

Close-up view of a Bulle movement showing the electric contact mechanism, circa 1921. (Photo courtesy of the Science Museum, London, England)

Globe model with French version of movement.

newer materials were incorporated when manufacture was begun in England in 1934. The most evident change was in the magnet which was made of cobalt steel and only 3/16" in diameter. Bobs were a metal disc with wood rods and the plates were stamped aluminum. Bakelite, a new material at that time, was used in the case in addition to the usual wood and some had chrome decorations.

Favre-Bulle, aged 84, died on April 24, 1954, having filed for more than thirty patents on various subjects. He left no descendants. Lavet who was a graduate of the Art et Metiers and l'Ecole Superioure d'Electricite, Paris became a Professor of l'Ecole Nationale Supoericure de l'Aeronauyique Paris. It was here he was associated with Messeur Hatot who adapted his discoveries, Lavet being the first to apply transistor control to balance wheels and pendulum.

Suggested Reading

1. Belmont, Henri, 1975: *LaBulle Clock*, 1st ed., Besancon, France, Editions Millot & Cie.

2. Lloyd-Jones FBHI, George E., 1977: The Bulle Clock, *Horological Journal*, May, pp. 28-30.

Dr. F.G.A. Shenton, #24861

Marguette model wall clock.

Crystal regulator model. *Left*, front view. *Right*, rear view.

Oak mantle model, English version. *Upper,* front view. *Lower,* rear view. Compare pendulum and magnet with French version.

"Classic" model. *Upper,* rear view with case opened to show the French style movement. *Lower,* front view. (Photo courtesy of Bill Ellison)

Mahogany mantle model, French version. *Upper,* front view. *Lower,* rear view with case opened to show movement. Compare with English version.

BULOVA WATCH COMPANY, INC.

Like many immigrants who came to America in the middle to late 1870's, Joseph E. Bulova opened a business in the profession he had learned in his native Czechoslovakia. The retail jewelry store which he opened in 1874 on Maiden Lane in New York City prospered and in 1877 he began manufacturing high-grade basic jewelry items there. It was only natural that he should expand into watches and, in 1907 he began importing watches from Switzerland. Four years later, he opened a factory in Providence, Rhode Island to manufacture watch cases and his expanding jewelry line.

Realizing that the trend was toward wrist watches after the end of World War I, the newly organized Bulova Watch Company introduced the first complete line of men's and ladies' jeweled-lever wrist watches. In 1919 the company established a watch factory in Bienne, Switzerland which was to serve them well for a number of years.

In the mid-1920s, using the new medium of radio, Bulova began what was

Accutron day-date Diver model with 218 movement. *Left,* dial view. *Right,* view of works.

Accutron blue marble and brass desk clock

the first series of "spot" announcements as a primary advertising campaign. "It's 9 p.m., B-U-L-O-V-A, Bulova Watch Time" came to be listened for and did much to establish the firm's name as a producer of accurate, dependable timepieces.

Seeing the war clouds gathering over Europe in the early 1930's and realizing that their source of movements from Switzerland might be cut off, Bulova began to train teams of research, design and production people and to establish integrated tool room and production facilities in the United States. Although the company did not produce entire watch movements domestically until after World War II, this pool of skilled craftsmen enabled the first to serve the war effort well. In all, they produced almost 50 million dollars worth of military watches and other timepieces, aircraft instruments, bomb fuses, telescopes, and torpedo parts.

Anticipating the future growth of the company, Bulova purchased a large acreage of wasteland near New York

City's LaGuardia Airport and created a new corporate headquarters in the early 1950s. Named "Bulova Park," its main structure was a new two-story factory/office building equaling in size many 40-story office buildings in area. It housed the firm's production facilities for their 21-, 23- and new 30-jewel watch movements, its corporate headquarters and the Joseph Bulova School of Watchmaking — the country's first industrial school for paraplegics.

After some eight years of development, Bulova introduced its revolutionary new timepiece, the Accutron, on October 26, 1960. Based on the combined work of Max Hetzel, originally of the firm's Bienne (Switzerland) plant but later to become the chief physicist at the US plant, and William O. Bennett, an engineer with the US operation, it utilized timekeeping principles never before used in a watch. The new design eliminated the usual mainspring, escapement, balance, hairspring and winding mechanism. It contained only 12 moving parts compared to 26 in a typical self-winding watch and only 27 parts in all versus 130, but one needed a microscope to work on the movement. The watch represented a melding of watchmaker skills, modern electronics and miniaturization and was to dominate the quality watch field for about ten years.

The Accutron was produced in a number of models ranging from eight to 15 jewels. Although designed as a wrist watch, Accutron movements were cased in a variety of ways: as wrist watches, pendant watches, nitestand clocks, carriage clocks, travel clocks and desk

Left, Accutron day-date model with 218 movement. *Right,* railroad approved Accutron with 214 movement.

Accutron clock with 214 movement in travel case.

clocks, to name a few. A Bulova Accutron timer, weighing just 8 ounces, replaced 30 pounds of equipment on the Explorer satellite which orbited the earth.

Bulova licensed the tuning-fork principle to ESA in Switzerland and they licensed Longines, Omega and Zenith to manufacture and sell tuning-fork watches. The Swiss utilized a balanced tuning fork in their products, which was slightly different from the Bulova and less prone to positional error.

With the increasing popularity of quartz timepieces, Bulova came on the market with its Accuquartz watch in 1970. It incorporated their tuning-fork concept with a quartz oscillating circuit and although the watches were marketed for several years the Accuquartz never achieved the success of the earlier Accutron. It was replaced by straight quartz movements.

Suggested Reading

1. Anonymous, 1966: The watch industry clocks a new record, *Business Week,* December 24.

2. Fried, Henry B., 1961: Repairing Bulova's "Accutron," *Jewelers' Circular Keystone,* February and March.

3. Bennett, W. O., 1969: Accutron — A Chronometric Micropower Plant, Reprinted in *Journal of Electrical Horology,* March, 1991.

G. Harry Blair, #37038
William F. Keller, #12745

Bulova Thermatron, a watch powered by body heat, introduced in England in 1983. See addendum

Bulova world time clock using a large tuning fork movement licensed by ATO. Clock shows daylight and dark hours on a paper tape.

DARCHE ELECTRIC CLOCK CO.

Though some would argue that the Darche Electric Clock Co. does not truly belong in a work on electric timekeeping, its products did depend on battery power for some of their functions, hence its inclusion here. Basically the clocks were simple spring-driven alarms with movements made by Waterbury and an electric component that rang a bell, lit a light or carried out some other function.

The clock firm was a successor to many other Darche operations in the Chicago area and the first address found for the Darche Clock Company per se was 648 W. 12th St. in Chicago, the same address as that of George C. Darche who was listed as a jeweler and shown as the firm's President. That was in 1896 and ties in with the date of July 5, 1892, when George received patent #478,155 for his "electric alarm clock." Over the next 30 or so years of its existence, the firm moved a number of times and had several name changes. By 1903 it was called the Darche Electric Clock Company and located at 803 S. Halsted St. A year later, George died and subsequently Frank Jansen took over as President until 1909.

During Jansen's presidency he registered the trademark "Searchlight" and his name appeared on some Darche clocks. The firm's alarm clocks, as we know them, were not the only products made during Jansen's service with the

Dittco model in wooden case with night light and wooden bulb switch.

Metal cased night light model with dappled copper finish and battery in horizontal position beneath clock.

firm for they also listed a "Medical Surgical" clock. One can only conjecture what this might have been and how it might have been used; perhaps it timed certain kinds of electro therapy, even shock therapy, but this is pure speculation. Following his period as President of the firm, Jansen appears to have started his own clock company in Chicago, although little is known of it.

The year 1909 saw something most unusual happen with the firm, a female Augusta Y. Darche — possibly George's widow, was named President. She continued as President until 1928 and had several patents issued in her name. Perhaps the most significant was a patent issued in 1917 for a "Reminder Clock" which was in reality a timer.

The Darche firm appears to have been a victim of the depression of 1929 since no records have been found beyond that period.

Suggested Reading

1. Anonymous, 1976: Darche Manufacturing Company (Alarm Clocks) (Electric Time Machine), *Journal of Electrical Horology*, May.

2. Rubin, J.Z., 1990: A Darche Mfg. Co. Clock, *NAWCC Bulletin*, 32:55.

Judith Z. Rubin #79399

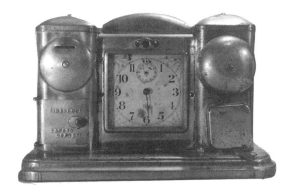

Silver-finish case with two pedestals, one a battery receptacle an the other a "fireproof safety" deposit. This is probably the model most often associated with Darche.

Medical-surgical model. Just how this was to be used is pure conjecture.

Heavy cast single-pedestal model with one bell.

Walnut cased model approximately 20 inches tall with heavy beveled glass in door.

◀ Catalog illustration of Rouser model.

Timelight model in wooden case with ▶ night light and wooden bulb switch.

DRAWBAUGH ELECTRIC CLOCK

Few are the NAWCC members who may have seen or even heard of the Drawbaugh Electric Clock for, indeed, few were ever manufactured. Be that as it may, we include it here as much because of the man as because of the clock itself. Daniel Drawbaugh was, we are told, a good clockmaker, but he was more than that. To some he was the "Wizard of Cumberland County (PA)" while to others he was "Crazy Drawbaugh." Based on what we and others have found, the former would seem to be the more appropriate epitaph for the man.

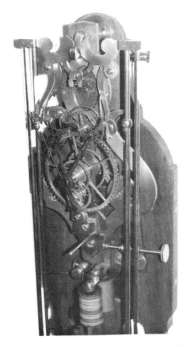

Detail of escapement and contact mechanism. (Photo courtesy of Art Bjornestad)

Patent model of movement. Note the steel and brass compensation rods and the unusual compensation mechanism. (Photo courtesy of Art Bjornestad)

Detail of pendulum bob-compensation mechanism. (Photo courtesy of Art Bjornestad)

Invented in the 1870's, the Drawbaugh Electric Clock was a ponderous piece and stood over six feet tall with a pendulum weighing almost 24 pounds. The pendulum was propelled by "an ingenious arrangement of permanent magnets and electromagnets" according to the late Jim Gibbs, who owned one of the clocks. Power for the electromagnets was dependent upon an earth battery — a well six feet deep lined with fine plates and filled with carbon. Ultimately, the earth battery proved a failure. It was seriously affected by electric storms and likely to be affected

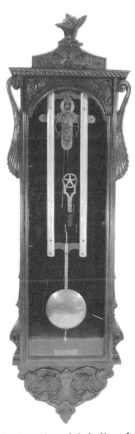

Unfinished wall model, believed to be Drawbaugh's last clock.

Drawbaugh was born in 1827 to Pennsylvania German parents and was trained in the trade of his father, a blacksmith. He was, by all reports a general handyman with an inventive bent who was granted his first patent at the age of 16 or 17 years. It was a patent for a process to expedite the making of iron wagon wheel rims. In his lifetime, Drawbaugh was granted a total of 125 patents and is said to have invented many other items which he never patented. One of his inventions was a telephone, invented in 1866, and perfected to a practical point in 1876, preceding Alexander Graham Bell by about ten years! It is reported that many of the independent telephone companies which were common in American cities up to about 1910 were the direct outgrowth of Drawbaugh's invention and it is known that he had a local telephone company. Unfortunately, when a showdown with the Bell interests came, they won a split decision in the courts after severe litigation and one of the longest opinions ever given by the United States Supreme Court up to that time.

by extraneous materials in the soil. Even though most of the clocks extant were modified for dry cell power, and even house current power, they were evidently too massive and cumbersome to be a success.

The Drawbaugh Clock was, in many ways, similar to the clock of Alexander Bain described in the *Massachusetts Ploughman* of June 19, 1847, but it clearly never met with the acclaim afforded Bain's work. Gibbs states that

DRAWBAUGH ELECTRIC CLOCK

Drawbaugh, himself, made only three clocks, one of which was exhibited in Harrisburg, Pennsylvania in 1874 at 10¢ a look. Other sources indicate that the clocks were made in three styles of casing: tall case, pedestal type and mural. The latter case was said to be in the form of a banjo and to have much carving in the early "Empire" style and only a few disfiguring elements of late Victorian style.

Very few of these clocks seem to be extant. If, indeed, a collector is fortunate enough to come upon one immediate purchase is recommended.

Suggested Reading

1. Anonymous, 1949: Concerning The Drawbaugh Electric Clock, *Timepieces Quarterly*, I:172-173.

2. Swetnam, G., 1961: Clockmakers and Watchmakers of Western Pennsylvania, *NAWCC Bulletin*, IX:547.

3. Gibbs, J.W., 1956: Daniel Drawbaugh, Tragic Genius, *NAWCC Bulletin*, VII 158-162.

William F. Keller, #12745

Electro Clock Company

Organized in 1909 by Sidney C. Vincent, the Electro Clock Company of Baltimore, Maryland had a relatively short life and their products are very seldom seen in Marts. Their 1912 catalog, published just a year before the firm's demise, lists a dozen different models, including tall case, wall and mantle examples in cases quite similar to those of other manufacturers. Many of the models had "seconds bits" and they all appear to have the same basic mechanism, whether they be long or short drop.

The clock was powered completely by gravity and no springs were involved. According to an article in *The American Jeweler* of July 1912, the electric gravity, horse shoe plate movement "is driven by a weight, and the weight is raised by an armature with angular movement. The driving weight, armature level, and contact cam are all mounted on the central arbor." The article states further, "...the contacts are big enough to stand a large amount of wear and sparking, and may be easily brightened and cheaply replaced.... the movement will be recognized as having been made by a well known factory, which insures its accuracy."

The clock was, indeed, a well-made and well-conceived movement, but the firm's products evidently suffered from the "bad" reputation of battery-powered clocks at the time it was introduced. This could well account for the considerable number of testimonial letters included in the catalog, including some from railroads and the House of Representatives — an effort to overcome this reputation.

Suggested Reading

1. DeVilbiss, Jere A., 1989: The Electro Clock, *NAWCC Bulletin*, 31:215-227.

2. Electro Clock Company, 1912: *The Electro Clock* (Catalog), Baltimore, MD.

Jere A. DeVilbiss, FNAWCC, #18616

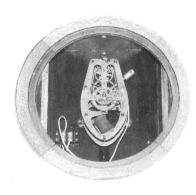

Modified model #1H (?) in oak. *Upper*, note the addition of the battery case at the bottom and the removal of the shield from top of bottom door. *Lower*, dial removed to show typical horseshoe works. (Photos courtesy of Lehr Dircks)

Standard model #1H in oak. Compare the position of the second bit with the clock to the right.

ELGIN WATCH COMPANY

In its long and distinguished history beginning in 1864, the Elgin Watch Company was responsible for many advances in watchmaking. One of the least known stories, however, is of the company's efforts to produce an electric wrist watch. Five years before the introduction of the first Hamilton electric, on March 19, 1952, Elgin unveiled its laboratory model. The Lord Elgin, grade 725, Electronic watch was the first watch of its kind ever built. Requiring no mainspring or winding mechanism, it was powered by the smallest motor and battery then available.

At the time the announcement was made by then Elgin President J.G. Shennan, several laboratory models had been made and the "energy capsule" (battery) which was said to contain enough power to keep the watch running for almost a year was smaller than a one-cent coin. The tiny motor produced one seventy-five millionth of a horsepower and required

very little energy to run properly. Ten million such watches, it was said, could be run from the power consumed by a single 100-watt light bulb. The grade 725 movement contained 15 jewels, had six adjustments and was 8/0 size.

According to information released in 1952, the prospect was for man's wrist watch of conventional size priced at about $100.00 if offered at that time. President Shennan indicated that this would limit it sales potential and that every effort was being made to get the price comparable with that of conventional watches. It was further stated that there were no plans for a ladies' watch since they were too small to accommodate the batteries and watch motors manufactured by Elgin.

Just how Elgin came into the electronic watch business is most interesting. In the early 1930s, the late T. Albert Potter, then President of Elgin, foresaw the need for a radically new product that would assert Elgin's leadership

over the keen competition from imported watches. George T. Ensign, Elgin's Research Director, was told to give the project high priority and Elgin sponsored a project with the Armour Research Foundation in Chicago to assist with the theory and design of the watch.

With the advent of World War II, work on the watch was restricted. Immediately after the war work was resumed, utilizing new technologic advances such as non-magnetic alloys and semi-conductive materials.

During its work on its electronic watch, Elgin learned that the Lip Watch Company of Besancon, France was also doing research on an electronic watch and the two firms agreed to exchange information. Even with the exchange, each continued its own research and each introduced its watch on March 19, 1952. The watches, however, differed in many mechanical and electric respects.

The Elgin watch actually reached the market in 1961, when it was distributed in limited quantities, to jewelry stores in the Chicago area. Shortly after its introduction, the stock was recalled, and the watch was never to be reintroduced. As a consequence, these watches are very scarce.

Subsequently, Elgin did get into the electric wrist watch market through the importation of Swiss-made movements.

(The author wishes to express his sincere appreciation to John Runciman (#59,578) for his help in the research and the photos included here.)

Suggested Reading

1. Benis, A. (ed), 1954: The Answer Box, *NAWCC Bulletin,* VI: 96-97.

2. Rondeau, René, 1989: *The Watch of the Future — The Story of The Hamilton Electric Watch,* Corte Madera, CA, René Rondeau.

3. Anonymous, 1952: The Watch of Tomorrow...Electronic Wrist Watch Developed by Elgin Runs on Stored Energy, *The American Horologist and Jeweler,* April.

Larry D. Harnden, Jr., #44592

Lord Elgin electronic watch. *Upper left,* dial view. *Upper right,* back-set movement model 725 showing holder for two batteries. *Lower,* close-up of 725 movement.

Upper left, close-up of oval-shaped back-set model 722 movement which is smaller than the model 725. *Upper right*, close-up of model 910 back-set movement, believed to be a prototype. *Lower right*, close-up of a stem-set movement, similar to a model 722, with no model number and believed to be a prototype. Note the difference in the balance wheel.

ETA ENGINEERS

By the early 1970's, after more than 95 years of supplying standard time information, the Western Union Company decided to sell its Time Service operation (see the paper on Self-Winding Clock Company). The number of subscribers had been steadily declining as more and more accurate timekeeping devices became available and numbered only 9,000 in 1972 compared to 100,000 in 1940. It was their thinking that a smaller company could possibly service the remaining market more effectively and profitably.

A number of Tucson, Arizona investors organized by entrepreneur J. Douglass Marshall expressed interest in the opportunity to take over the service and eventually purchased it. The group incorporated in Arizona as Radio Time Service, Inc. (RTS) with several

Standard radio-controlled ETAclock model with a black background, white hands and sequentially lighted LEDs supplementing the sweep-second hand.

local business and professional men as owners, including this author, who was technical advisor to the group.

The original RTS concept was to supply correction signals to quartz-crystal-controlled wall clocks by radio signals broadcast from commercial AM broadcast stations. The signal from the station was to be derived from the extremely accurate signals broadcast by WWV, a 24-hour-a-day time service provided by the National Bureau of Standards (NBS), recently renamed the National Institute of Standards and Technology (NIST).

The signal received would activate a device (e.g., a solenoid) in the RTS clock to bring it into synchronization with WWV. The signal utilized would be an audio tone, simply encoded, to prevent accidental "correction" by normal commercial programming. It was thought that the entire United States could be served by a relatively small number of carefully selected clear-channel AM broadcast stations.

This correction method would have permitted the use of small inexpensive transistor radios, mounted behind the face of the clock, to receive the WWV signal. A small simple electronic circuit would have been added to decode and apply the correction impulse to the clock mechanism. RTS contracted with the Westclox Division of General Time Corporation to modify their Quartzmatic Model C wall clocks to permit correction by such an external signal. For its part, Westclox agreed to provide the clocks in sufficient numbers to permit RTS to function as a supplier to accurate time. It was intended that the clocks be sold, rather than leased.

The RTS radio broadcast proposal incurred immediate opposition from the Federal Communications Commission (FCC), which chose to classify the update signal as a "point-to-point" communication. Under FCC rules, such transmissions are regarded as telephone company functions which must not be infringed under any circumstances by commercial radio stations. Repeated violations of this rule can cost a station its license. NBS, attempting to be helpful, pointed out that there is a specific exception under FCC rules which permits transmission of the WWV time tone, provided no commercial message is associated with the broadcast. After twenty-four hours of legal conferences and precedent searches, the FCC ruled that such a transmission, even without a commercial message, was still a point-to-point transmission simply because it was "sponsored". When pressed, they admitted they were on very shaky legal ground. If challenged, however, they promised to use the Federal Court System to delay any possible favorable decision for years. This had the intended effect of denying the applicant the proposed use of the technique. So much for the Federal cooperation with small business!

At this point Radio Time Service was faced with a decision — should the project be dropped, or should attempts be made to correct the clock by some

other means which did not involve the FCC. After a short study, it was decided to continue the product and attempt to utilize signals received at the clock directly from WWV. This alternative was made more difficult by the fact that small inexpensive receivers capable of receiving the WWV signals were unavailable at the time, and that no real knowledge of the radio-signal strength required to correct the clock was available. On the plus side, however, was the fact that the FCC could be completely bypassed.

In contrast to the FCC, the National Bureau of Standards was most cooperative during the entire ordeal and provided along with other useful information, reliability tables for predicting the usability of WWV transmissions throughout the western hemisphere. On the basis of these statistics, the 10 MHz frequency was chosen as the most likely to be received all over the United States. As it turned out, the choice was an excellent one.

A 10 MHz receiver that would fit inside the clock case behind the dial was developed, along with electronic circuits to separate the desired update tone from other signals and speech which are present on the WWV transmissions. Early clocks developed for this use carried both the RTS and the Westclox logos. To the casual observer, they were otherwise indistinguishable from the Westclox Model C. These models did, however, contain an incandescent pilot light mounted behind the RTS logo on the face of the clock. Upon update, the light would glow for a short period of time to indicate that a correction had occurred. No audio signals were available to the customer.

Small radio-controlled mantle clock with a digital readout for hours and minutes and a scoreboard-type seconds indicator.

Although the clock went though significant minor design changes over the next few years, primarily in the electronics to make WWV audio available, externally it continued to appear very similar to the original models. No additional changes were made until RTS decided to quit the business in 1979-80. The basic reason given by RTS for leaving the accurate time field were essentially the same as those given by Western Unions six or seven years earlier — there was, indeed a market, but the talent required to service it could better by utilized in other, more profitable, ventures.

In 1980 the STS function was taken over by ETA Engineers, a consulting service founded in 1962 and still operating under the sole proprietorship of the author. The primary service offered to clock customers was maintenance and repair of existing clocks, although a few new clocks were sold during the next six years.

Since acquiring the clock service, ETA Engineers has spent some time in the development of an all electronic display which would simulate the rotary motion of an analog clock. No commercially satisfactory product has yet been developed using this principle. In the interim, however, ETA Engineers has provided a much improved hybrid quartz-crystal mechanical clock with 60 sequentially lighted LEDs provided information previously obtained from a sweep-second hand. The design also features much reduced susceptibility to electrical interference. A black dial and oversize white hands provide improved readability from a distance. The clock has been available since 1986 and is being used primarily in the dispatching function of bus transportation companies also by radio and television stations.

Both RTS and ETA used Westclox movements and cases. Since these are no longer available, ETA now used movements supplied either by Kienzle (Germany) or Primex (Lake Geneva, Wisconsin) and adds the correcting feature in Tucson. Current designs include mantle and desk models in addition to wall clocks. All are available on special order from the company.

Alfred Hoehn, Ph.D., P.E.

EUREKA CLOCK CO.

The Eureka Battery Clock is associated through patent records with the names Kutnow and Powers. The basic design was by Timothy Powers, an electrical engineer of 853 Broadway, New York City and it would appear that the Kutners were involved mainly in providing financial assistance for the manufacture of the clock and in its marketing.

Sigismund, Herman and Gustav Kutnow first appear in the street directories of London as Manufacturing Agents and Commission Agents at Australian Avenue, before moving to Gresham St. and subsequently to Holborn Viaduct on the corner of Snow Hill. While at this latter address in 1894 they changed the nature of their business to that of Manufacturing Chemists, gaining much of their fame from Kutnow's Carlsbad Powders, "Prescribed for and used by the British Royal Family."

The choice of the name "Eureka" of Archimedian fame for the clock seemed to imply that the Kutnows thought they had hit the jack pot and they took out worldwide patents in at least thirteen countries: #14,614 in Great Britain was dated June 26, 1906 and #853,648 in the United States dated May 14, 1907.

The Eureka Clock Company, 361-363 Coty Road, London EC was formed and registered in December, 1908 by the Kutnows and Frank Jewett, the latter becoming the company secretary. Marketing of the Eureka Clock began early in 1909 and in July of that year and Sigismund Kutnow presented a representative clock to King Edward VII for his inspection. About 10,000 clocks were produced during a five-year period ending a few days prior to the declaration of World War I. The company decided on July 27, 1914 to go into voluntary liquidation and a final winding-up meeting was held on April 12, 1916 with patent rights lapsing in 1918.

Mention should be made of the patents that were issued for a striking version of the clock by L. Asprey and E. Farrow (UK Patent #26,194, November 14, 1912) which specifically relates to a striking mechanism applicable to clocks of the UK Patent #14614 (1906). There is no evidence to date that this striking clock was ever produced. The single

Tall four-glass wood case (English) model, circa 1914. Note the balance wheel below the dial. (Photo courtesy of Charles K. Aked)

Short version of four-glass wooden case (English) model. *Upper*, front view. *Lower*, back view showing balance wheel behind dial.

Cromwellian lantern model (English). *Upper*, front view. *Lower*, case door opened to show works.

Eureka striker recorded does not conform to the 1906 patent and it is this author's opinion that the striking portion of the clock in question was a conjectural experimental production model in which the striking portion was added to a standard factory model.

Timothy Bernard Powers, engineer and the Eureka Clock Co., 361 City Road, London secured a further electric clock patent (UK #4711, February 24, 1911; US Patent #1,012,010, December 19, 1911) for an electrically wound model. Only one known example has been recorded, a very well made elegant factory production. It is possible others may have survived.

Globe model (German), circa 1921. Note similarity to English models and the stamped rather than cast plates. *Upper*, front view with globe in place. *Right*, rear view with globe removed.

Wood-cased Sheraton model (English). *Left*, front view. *Right*, rear view with door open to show battery case.

Brass cased Madelaine model (English).
(Photo courtesy of Tran Duy Ly)

Following the extraordinary General Meeting of the firm on December 7, 1909, Sigismund Kutnow was given authority to sell, at his discretion, patent rights that had been granted abroad. There is little doubt that the German patents were sold, since two of the largest shareholders outside the Kutnow family were Maximillion Ekert, a merchant of Hamburg, and Martin Duisberg, a Berlin manufacturer. A variation of the Eureka clock was made in Germany, possibly for only that year. The German clocks were of lesser quality than those made in England. Different materials, stamped plates and a different contact arrangement were used, and the balance wheel was machined differently. As far as is known only one style was made — a tall domed model.

A third type of Eureka was manufactured in Germany about 1935 and distributed in the United States by the Forestville Clock Company. It had a transformer located in the base which delivered 3 volts DC to the clock from a 110 volt AC power source. Few intact examples exist today since most eventually stopped when the contacts froze, burning up because there was no fuse or other protective device. These clocks more closely resemble the original Eurekas since they have a larger balance wheel than other German-made models.

Suggested Reading

1. Shenton, Dr. F.G. Alan, 1979: *The Eureka Clock*, 1st Ed., Twickenham (England), Rita Shenton Publisher.

2. Mid-West Electrical Group (NAWCC), 1983: *Eureka Clock Catalog*, Chicago, IL, Mid-West Electrical Group.

3. De Mognin, Paul Ro, 1963: Collecting Battery-Powered Clocks, *NAWCC Bulletin*, X:709-710.

4. Anonymous, 1983: Eureka Clocks, *Clocks*, March, pp. 24-29.

Dr. F.G.A. Shenton, #24861

FRED FRICK CLOCK COMPANY

This brief history might be better entitled, "The McCaskey/Frick/Landis Saga", since the history of the three firms all located in Waynesboro, Pennsylvania was intertwined and, one might say, a continuing story. It was in the late 1880's that J.L. McCaskey came to that small town in Pennsylvania to be the supervising principal of their first high school. Being an ingenious sort, he conceived the idea of ringing school bells by placing contacts on the hands of a clock and received his first patent for same in 1890.

McCaskey's system, even with the improvements he patented in 1891 and 1894, did not function in the manner he had hoped. Accordingly, he went to Fred Frick, a local engineer asking his help in accomplishing his goal. Frick, designed an improved system, bought out McCaskey and formed his own company — The Fred Frick Clock Company. In August 1894, the new firm began to produce program clocks of Frick's design using basic spring-driven movements purchased from Seth Thomas and Howard, modified to accept the program mechanism for which Frick received his first two patents in 1895. His program clock utilized a disc with many holes and pins to fit in those holes, thus permitting the operator to change the time of any activity simply by moving the pins to a new and proper position. The clocks were used primarily in schools and factories to ring bells and to turn lights on and off and were sold to schools as far from Waynesboro as New York City; Greeley, Colorado; and Ellensburg, Washington.

During this same period Frick sold many non-program office clocks using cases his company manufactured for his program masters. These clocks had unmodified purchased movements, often with the original movement manufacturer's name still on it and either brass or painted dials installed bearing the name Fred Frick Clock Co., Waynesboro, PA., U.S.A. on them. Later, Frick developed a battery-powered "self-winding" clock to be used in offices, stores, etc. According to a local Waynesboro source, the cast iron movements with steel bushings in these clocks were designed by Frick, but we have been unable to find a patent or verify this in any way. This new "self-

Frick patent self-winding store regulator model. *Upper,* front view. *Lower,* dial removed to show self-winding mechanism.

Frick five-minute program clock with Seth Thomas spring-driven movement hanging in NAWCC Museum. *Upper,* front view. *Lower,* close-up of movement and program mechanism.

Landis wood-cased secondary (slave). (Photo courtesy of Lehr Dircks)

"winding" movement was also used in his program clocks and was the same movement that Landis later used, as evidenced by an illustration in their catalog and those of their clocks we have examined.

Landis patent one-minute program mechanism in a separate case.

Frick self-winding clock. Both Frick and Landis models were cased in these "Seth Thomas # 2" cases.

Catalog illustration of patented self-winding movement used by both Frick and Landis. Note the cast iron plates and bushed pivots.

Landis patent slave mechanism used by Cincinnati Time.

In 1910 Frick sold his business to F.F. Landis, another local inventor and entrepreneur, who installed his son Mark as the company's Manager and Chief Engineer. F.F. Landis was another with an inventive bent who held over 100 patents. Many of Landis' patents related to the design of the clock's slave movements or to the refinement of the program mechanism by using a drum which permitted programming in minute rather than five-minute intervals as did the Frick models. It was also during the Landis period that a patent was granted for a mercury pendulum to be used on the master clock. This permitted the clocks to meet the exacting standards of the U.S. Bureau of Standards.

In 1930, the Landis Program Clock Co. firm went into receivership and J.G. Mumma, a local banker, managed the company from 1932 until it was sold in 1937 to the Cincinnati Time Recording Co. It is interesting to note that most, if not all, of the Cincinnati slaves we have encountered, even if sold before the takeover, were of the same fundamental design as those made by Landis indicating that they were probably purchased from that firm. Some even carry a Landis patent number and the Landis name.

Much of the history of these firms remains obscure, but we do know that they made full use of any materials that may have been in inventory when a successor firm took over. It is interesting, but not unusual, to see Landis master clocks with Landis name plates and Frick labelled components or Cincinnati name plates on clocks with Cincinnati dials and Landis labelled program mechanisms.

Suggested Reading

1. Carbaugh, T., 1985: Fred Frick Clock Company, *NAWCC Bulletin*, XXVII: 53-55.

2. Gibbs, James, W., 1984: *Pennsylvania Clocks and Watches*, University Park, PA, The Pennsylvania State University Press.

William F. Keller #12745

GENERAL MOTORS AUTOMOTIVE CLOCKS

Electric clocks intended for automobiles have a long history. As early as 1915, advertisements described electrically wound clocks powered by dry cells separate from the automobile's electric system. As automotive electric systems switched from magneto ignition systems to battery ignition systems and the electric self-starter became more common, the automobile's electric system became more suitable to power a clock. Electric automobile clocks freed the stylist from the need to provide for winding the clock and electric clocks were preferred, particularly for the high-priced autos.

In the early 1920's automotive electric clocks tended to be mechanical clocks which were powered by a spring, periodically wound by a solenoid. Although generally good timekeepers, they suffered from problems with the electric contacts, particularly when the high current flows necessitated by 6-volt electric systems are considered.

By the early 1950's, the problems with both timekeeping and reliability led to the development of two new approaches. One, developed by General Motors, involved the use of a small direct current motor which replaced the mainspring in supplying power to the balance wheel. This motor could operate for long periods in or very near a stalled position. Though its use in

Rear-view mirror with electric clock listed as an extra for GM cars.

automobiles was relatively brief such motors are currently in common use in the paper feed systems of plain paper copiers.

The second approach also developed by General Motors used a magnetic field activity directly on the balance wheel as a means of powering the clock. The balance wheel of these clocks was very carefully shaped to take full advantage of the magnetic force available. The weak point of these clocks was the very small springs which formed the electric contacts triggering the magnetic pulses.

Both approaches were soon abandoned, probably because of their higher cost when compared to the electrically wound mechanical clocks. The adoption of the 12-volt electrical systems gave electrically wound, mechanical clocks a short reprieve, but cost pressures resulted in the use of a low quality clock which was quite unreliable.

The use of a quartz crystal to control a "stepper motor" to drive the clock hands followed. Though these clocks offered much better reliability and improved timekeeping, they were not the "space-aged chronometers which required resetting only when you change time zones" advertised by one automobile manufacturer. These were the last automotive clocks to contain some mechanical parts.

Electronic digital clocks were soon commonly used, first as separate units which were necessary to fill the dashboard "holes" intended for the previously used mechanical clocks; then as part of the radio which required a quartz timing circuit for tuning. Today, automotive clocks are universally incorporated in the radio and collectable automotive clocks are probably a thing of the past.

Suggested Reading

1. Ellison, H.W., 1985: Untapped Sources of Electro-Mechanical Clocks Discovered, *The Journal of Electrical Horology*, October.

2. Zimmer, J., 1985: Car Clocks, *NAWCC Bulletin*, XXVII:725.

3. Kotis, A.F.T., 1976: Marine Chronometer History, *NAWCC Bulletin*, XVIII:85.

H. William Ellison, FNAWCC, #35143

HADDON PRODUCTS, INC.

Little information is available on Haddon Products, Inc. of Chicago which manufactured and sold Golden Vision, Commodore, Golden Visionette, and Sun Gold'n Hour clocks, among others, in the 1950s and 1960s. Many of their clocks carry no Patent number, but we have seen one with #2,843,999 on the bottom plate, some 200,000 patents after Jefferson Electric's patent on their Golden Hour. It would appear, therefore, that Jefferson and Haddon models were manufactured and sold during roughly the same period of time. This plus the fact that many Haddon models are so similar in appearance to Jefferson's, gives further credence to the generally held opinion that they were designed to compete with the popular

Golden Visionette model. Note the similarity to the Jefferson Golden Hour. *Left*, Front view. *Right*, bottom of case showing the "stamped label." (Photo courtesy of Harry Bredfeldt)

Sun Gold'n Hour model.

Commodore model. (Photo courtesy of Harry Bredfeldt)

Jefferson models, but at a somewhat lower price.

Both clock lines were powered by a synchronous motor in the base and are similar in overall appearance, but here the similarity ends. The Jefferson models have a moving glass to which the minute hand is friction fitted and in front of the glass. The counterbalanced hour hand is behind the glass. The Haddon clocks have a wire "finger" extending from the outermost end of the minute hand which fits into a geared ring at the outer edge of the glass dial. The glass on the Haddon is fixed and both minute and hour hands are in front of the glass.

According to Jesse Coleman, the problems seen with the Haddon clocks were inherent in their basic design because of their "peculiar construction, plus (their) running of like metals (brass on brass) together." Coleman stated that careful greasing is required.

Just how long the clocks were manufactured and how many is a question. We do know, however, that they were sold from the mid-1950s and well into the 1960s. Further research on the Haddon Company may yield definitive answers to these and other questions. It would also be of interest to know whether any members of the firm were ever affiliated with Jefferson since both companies were located in Chicago and the product lines were so similar.

Suggested Reading

1. Hagans, Orville, R., (ed), 1979: *The Best of J.E. Coleman: Clockmaker*, Denver, CO, The American Watchmaker's Institute Press, p. 303.

2. Heffner, Paul, (ed), 1991: The Answer Box, *NAWCC Bulletin*, 33: 327-328.

William F. Keller, #12745

HAMILTON WATCH COMPANY

Although electricity has been used in clockmaking for generations, watchmakers could only dream of eliminating the mainspring. With no batteries small enough to fit inside a watch case, the dream could not become a reality. The turning point came as a result of World War II research, when miniature batteries developed for the military became available to the public.

The first company to bring the elusive dream of an electric watch to reality was the Hamilton Watch Company in Lancaster, PA. In 1946, Hamilton's President, George Luckey, assigned the project of developing such a watch to Arthur Fillinger in their Research & Development Department. Fillinger ultimately designed an electric timepiece in which an electromagnet powered the balance wheel, which in turn drove the rest of the gear train. Because miniature batteries were still not commercially available, he built a model of his movement as a small clock. Nonetheless, he submitted a patent claim under the designation "Electric Watch" in 1947. Hamilton's management took great pride in their

first patent for an electric timepiece, granted in 1951. Fillinger worked on his model for nearly two years before transferring to another division. His successor, John Hendricks, continued experimenting, but despite their best efforts, the watch/clock remained unreliable.

In 1950, Fred Koehler, a master technician considered to be Hamilton's finest watchmaker, took over the project. He had frequently been called upon to make parts for and repair the Fillinger models, and understood the limitations of the movement. He constructed a far superior movement which retained the electromagnetically powered balance wheel, but was otherwise completely redesigned. Like Fillinger, Koehler built his model as a clock but submitted a patent application under the title "Electric Watch" in October, 1951. His movement became known as the "Koehler Clock," and was highly regarded in the Research Department for its accuracy — called "equal to or better than that of a railroad watch" in a 1952 Hamilton memo.

Railroad approved wrist watch with a 500 movement.

In 1952, Koehler took the next step and assembled a handmade, watch-sized prototype in which a circular string of coils surrounded the movement, with a battery fitted into the back of the case. Known as EM-1, it was the first battery-powered wrist watch made at Hamilton. Unfortunately, though it was accurate, it consumed too much battery power to be practical.

Shortly before the Koehler prototype had been completed, the Elgin Watch Company announced its intention to produce and market an electric watch. This motivated Hamilton's chief physicist, Dr. John A. Van Horn, to take a closer look at the project. He proposed to Hamilton's management that the development work be given top priority, with the goal of producing the world's first electric watch. The Directors agreed and the project was assigned to Philip E. Biemiller, a talented physicist in Van Horn's division and James H. Reece, a brilliant inventor who had the rare talent of turning vague concepts into working models. This three-man team devoted the next decade to developing a marketable watch.

Van Horn felt that Koehler's electromagnetic system, with its fixed coil and moving magnets, was not suitable for a wrist watch because of its high energy requirements. He proposed a movement with a coil on the balance wheel moving within a permanent magnetic field.

Koehler's watch was abandoned, but his clock movement was used as the basis for the Hamilton Cordless Clock, an abortive attempt to make and market a battery desk clock. After six years of development and well over $100,000 invested, the cordless clock was scrapped in 1959. Koehler's original movement had been so stripped in an attempt to keep production costs low that it was no longer reliable.

Van Horn, Biemiller and Reece built their first working prototype of a moving coil electric watch in February, 1953. Because the balance wheel took up so much room, the battery was fitted in the strap. Further refinements led to a smaller balance and more efficient timekeeping. After three years and countless obstacles, the Model 500 was created. It was subjected to extensive "wear testing" by

Titan model with 505 movement. *Left*, dial view. *Right*, view of movement.

Electronic date model.

Hamilton employees, with only limited success. The development team redesigned most of the weak points, but by mid-1956 Hamilton's management became impatient and fearful that another company, particularly Elgin, would market an electric watch first. Consequently, the inventors were under extreme pressure to get the watch ready for market, despite its being an unrefined prototype.

On January 3, 1957, Hamilton held a press conference to announce the "World's First Electric Watch," though

the watches themselves did not hit the stores until March. The idea of a watch that never needed winding appealed to the 1950s consumers, who were captivated by progress and modernity. The watch was an instant hit and its popularity was enhanced by the dramatic case styles with untraditional asymmetrical styling that were used. The cases were visual reminders of the ultramodern movement inside them.

Unfortunately, the physical limitations of the crude contact system and the complete lack of dealer training led to an overwhelming problem as customer's watches stopped and jewelers had to return them to the factory for servicing. Hamilton's reputation with the jewelry trade began to deteriorate.

By 1961, when Hamilton released its Model 505, a well-designed and very reliable movement, the damage had been done. The excitement of producing the world's first electric watch had worn off, and Hamilton faced the stigma of a temperamental watch that intimidated many watchmakers. When Bulova announced the Accutron, with a tuning fork replacing the balance wheel of the Hamilton electric, another nail was driven in Hamilton's coffin.

The lifespan of the Hamilton electric watch was brief, but it spanned the most exciting and tumultuous decade of the century, from the launch of Sputnik — the first space satellite to man's first step on the moon. When it was first released in 1952, it was "the watch of the future," but unfortunately for Hamilton the future passed them faster than anyone could have imagined. By 1969, when production ended, the world's first electric watch had become a quaint electromechanical relic.

Suggested Reading

1. Rondeau, René, 1989: *The Watch of the Future*, Corte Madera, CA, Published by the Author.

2. Rondeau, René, 1991: The Hamilton "Cordless" Clock, *NAWCC Bulletin*, 33:529-536.

3. Rondeau, René, 1991: Dials Crafted of Natural Wood — Hamilton Sherwood Watches, *NAWCC Bulletin*, 33:251-255.

Rene Rondeau, #89630

HAMMOND CLOCK COMPANY

Organized in April, 1928 and incorporated in May 1930, the Hammond Clock Co. became the Hammond Instrument Company in 1937. By 1938 it had gross sales of $1,243,429 according to *Moody's Manual of Investments*. Its plant was located in Chicago and the firm manufactured small electric motors, an electric organ and a patented electric bridge table in addition to its clocks. In late 1930, the company in cooperation with the DeForest Crosley Radio Company, Ltd. formed a subsidiary to manufacture and distribute electric clocks in Canada under Hammond patents.

Although there is little published information on this firm and its products, it is known that they supplied clock motors to Sessions Clock and possibly other companies. Hammond clocks were originally of the manual start variety and later self-start motors

Early manual-start (lever) synchronous mantle clock.

"Stewardess" model manual-start synchronous kitchen clock.

appeared. There was a quite large variety of styles and cases in the line, both phenolic and wood cases. Both synchronous and "Bichronous" movements were offered, often in like cases and some desk or mantel clocks had a day/date indicator at the bottom of the case beneath the clock dial.

"Cathedral" cased manual-start synchronous clocks. *Upper*, time only model. *Lower*, alarm model.

Day-date models in bakelite cases. *Upper*, manual-start art deco synchronous model. *Lower*, self-start Bichronous model.

Three Bichronous self-start models. *Upper*, tambour. *Middle*, Postal Telegraph. *Lower*, day-date alarm.

By far the most famous, or infamous (take your pick), were those clocks with the Hammond Bichronous movement. This movement incorporated a spring-drive mechanism in addition to the usual synchronous motor. Through the use of an ingenious braking arrangement the spring, when completely wound by the synchronous motor, is maintained in the wound state until such time as there might be a power interruption. When the interruption occurs, the "brake" releases and the power of the spring keeps the clock running for 30 minutes or so. Many large round wall clocks in metal cases with the Bichronous movement were sold to the Postal Telegraph system which was a competitor to Western Union in the telegraphic business in the 1920s and 1930s.

Suggested Reading

1. Hagans, Orville R., (ed), 1979: *The Best of J.E. Coleman: Clockmaker*, Denver, CO, American Institute Press, pp. 426-427, 440.

William F. Keller, #12745

Hansen Manufacturing Co.

Like so many of the early program clock firms, the Hansen company can trace its origins to a school official's request that a small-town jeweler build a program clock for his institution. That first clock, produced in 1906, was an Ansonia regulator modified by Julius W. Hansen in the rear of his jewelry store. The clock, installed in the Patoka (IN) High School, met with critical acclaim and became the harbinger of many more to come.

Encouraged by the success of his first "product," Hansen opened a small factory in 1907 and began manufacturing the Hansen Program Clock System. The company prospered under his direction, expanded into larger quarters on two occasions, and his son William eventually joined the firm. Just as they were about to announce a self-winding clock, World War I intervened and William went into the Army. The war, his son's absence, and the lack of the basic materials needed by the factory might well have spelled the death knell of the firm, but the senior Hansen persevered and kept the doors of the factory open by making a few items for the war effort.

The war over, father and son were reunited and, pooling their meager resources, managed to reopen the clock business. Soon, Hansen Program Clocks and the new Hansen self-winding models were in production and the firm was once again flourishing. Then, in 1925, a devastating tornado hit Princeton, leveling the factory and even blowing away the materials that had been accumulated for a planned addition.

Disheartened, perhaps, but still evidencing the puck of their Danish ancestors, the Hansens rebuilt the factory and within two years introduced their first synchronous motor. That motor named the "Synchron" was to become the firm's standard bearer. Its wide use in other clocks, timing devices, etc. surprised even the Hansens.

During the mid-1930s the firm enjoyed such success with its Synchron motors that the program clock operation was all but ignored. Then, in 1935, about a year before senior Hansen's death, the program clock operation was sold to Arvid N. Montgomery, an electrical engineer, from Owensville, Indiana.

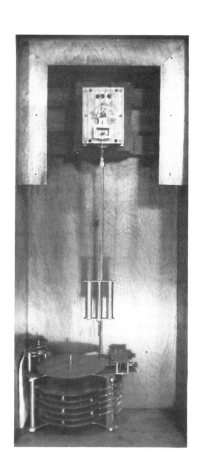

Master clock. *Upper,* front view. *Lower,* door opened to show program mechanism in bottom of case.

With a small inventory of parts and a gear cutter, moved from Princeton, Montgomery Time Systems opened its doors in Owensville. The new business began by soliciting repair jobs from known users of Hansen systems, a seemingly ready and immediate source of income for the firm in a period of depression when there was little market for new systems.

As funds began to become available, and as Montgomery's reputation grew based on its repair services, sales of program systems expanded until the advent of World War II. At that time, Arvil Montgomery sold nearly all the firm's raw materials and machinery, locked up the doors and accepted an offer of a Naval commission.

Immediately upon his return from service in 1945, Montgomery began preparations to reopen the firm. Purchasing used equipment and borrowing some until new equipment was available, he reopened in October, 1945. Following several years of successful operation, including a number of newly patented products, the company was incorporated in 1959.

The period since World War II has seen an ever increasing use of Montgomery automatic controls, whether they be for controlling signals in schools or factories, ringing church bells, irrigation or lawn sprinkling, air conditioning and heating, or for controlling manufacturing processes. Montgomery manufactured timing equipment for all these and many others, continuing the solid reputation established by the Hansen firm over 80 years ago. Meanwhile, the Hansen company continues to produce its Synchron motors, many of which are used in the very timing equipment Montgomery and others manufacture.

Suggested Reading

1. Anonymous, 1949: Hansen Manufacturing Observes Founder's Day, *Princeton* (IN) *Democrat,* February 27.

2. Anonymous, 1980: Clockmaker prelude to Hansen's opening, *Princeton Daily Clarion,* January 31.

3. Anonymous, 1989–1990: Hansen Manufacturing Company, Catalog #10, December-March.

William F. Keller, #12745

The Herschede Hall Clock Co.

Frank Herschede, the founder of the Herschede Hall Clock Co., began his business career in 1873, apprenticing himself to Charles Cook who owned a jewelry, watch and clock shop in Cincinnati. Four years later, he opened a business of his own at the age of twenty in an arcade which catered to the "trade."

Just what kindled his interest in hall clocks is not known, but a catalog published in the later half of the 1880's indicates he was an importer of English Hall Clocks. Cases for the clocks appear to have been made by a local cabinet maker whose business he later purchased. A number of movements were offered including some made by J.J. Elliott and others by Walter Durfee.

When his sons began to enter the business, Herschede decided that it was time to organize the clockmaking side properly and the Herschede Hall Clock Company was formally incorporated in December, 1902. During the next year Directors were appointed, rules drawn up, and capitalization completed. Frank Herschede's younger brother, John, who began his career as an engraver, was named President.

In January, 1909 a decision to manufacture its own movements was reached by the Board and a building was leased for this expansion. The movement department was organized under son Walter's direction and by the end of 1910 the first 100 tubular movements had been assembled. All other movements continued to be imported. World War I saw a dramatic increase in Herschede's business because they were making their own movements rather than relying on imported movements as many of their competitors did. Even though the firm dedicated a portion of its facilities to the making of surgical and hospital equipment, compasses and surveying instruments, clock manufacturing continued throughout the war.

During the early to mid-1920s public interest in electric timekeeping was closely watched by the company. Believing the idea was not sufficiently tested and that possible public dissatisfaction could discredit the respected Herschede name, President Walter Herschede was reluctant to move too fast. In 1926, however, he solved the

Early Revere Westminster chime tambour, auxiliary powered. The Revere name appears beneath the chapter ring and "Telechron Powered" appears above the center post.

Revere Westminster chime tambour carrying the Revere above the center post.

problem by organizing the Revere Clock Company to market electric clocks.

All Revere clocks were "Telechron-Motored" by Warren Telechron's synchronous motors and the two firms planned and carried out a cooperative advertising program. Further evidence of the cooperation of the two is seen in the manufacture of certain clock parts by Revere (Herschede) for Telechron. Although most of the clocks manufactured by Revere were mantle and boudoir models, some hall clocks equipped with an auxiliary spring mechanism which would keep the clock running for thirty-six hours during power interruption were also made.

A year or so later, with the success of the Revere line very evident, Walter Herschede decided to market electrically-driven Herschede floor clocks under the Herschede name. The firm also experimented with electrically-wound spring-driven Herschede models, but far fewer of these made their way into the trade than the Revere models. During this period, Herschede also made a line of electric clocks on contract for General Electric and that firm became the largest single account of the company. As an interesting sidelight,

Jesse Coleman wrote that on a visit to the Herschede plant he found that in the final operation clocks were Herschede, Revere or General Electric depending on which dial was fitted on the clock. How similar to many factories today, different labels on the same product.

As the depression spread across the country, Herschede felt the effects of it and developed a full line of electrics under the Herschede name in the hope of increasing sales, but it did not help. Finally, in 1933, a line of inexpensive electrics, Crown Clocks, was introduced, but it was to last only a year or so. Telechron enlarged its production capabilities in 1934 and no longer needed to purchase parts from Herschede, but an increase in sales to General Electric helped to balance that loss. Also, during the middle thirties the firm entered into an agreement with the Parkrite and Karpark companies to make parking meters, eventually securing a financial interest in Karpark which took over Parkrite.

Round gothic synchronous motor driven Westminster chime mantle clock with spring-driven chime.

Although Herschede's clock production during World War II was limited to making parts for repair work, a new sister firm, the Panocular Corporation was organized to make prismatic lenses, among other optical items needed for the war effort. After the war there was a great push to manufacture clocks to fill the pipelines and shelves which had been emptied during the war. In addition to their own products and the clocks they were supplying General Electric, the firm manufactured striking clocks for Telechron under contract. Then, in 1948,

The Herschede Hall Clock Co.

General Electric announced that it would purchase the Warren Telechron firm to provide a source for its electric alarm and clock radios. This meant the end of a most important contract of the Herschede Company for over twenty years.

With the outbreak of the Korean War, government contracts were again sought and secured, one was for periscopes to be used on tanks and Panocular was again activated. When the war ended in 1956, Herschede, which had been importing complete clocks under the Herschede label from Junghans, was making only hall or floor case models. A search for new products to supplement their clock production ensued, but nothing of interest developed. Meanwhile, a search for a location where costs would be lower than in Cincinnati was begun and Starkville, Mississippi was selected as the new

Synchronous alarm.

site. The move there in 1960, although it prolonged the life of the company, did not prove the panacea that management had hoped. Tubular chime and electric movements were made and cased in the new plant, but other movements continued to be imported. Although new government contracts were negotiated and several new products

were examined, nothing helped the cash position of the firm and in 1967 it was once again in serious financial straits. Revitalization via the purchase of a controlling interest by a Starkville business man helped revive the firm for a time, but it was to be formally closed some twenty years later after a lone and respected history.

Suggested Reading

1. Gibbs, James W., 1990: Tidbits from J.E. Coleman, *NAWCC Bulletin*, 32:133.

2. Hagans, Orville R., 1979: *The Best of J.E. Coleman: Clockmaker*, The American Watchmakers Institute Press, Denver, CO, pp. 80-83, 356-357.

3. Martines, Joseph E., 1977: Contemporary Clockmaking: An Overview, *NAWCC Bulletin* XIX:578, 584.

Howard Klein, #40522

E. HOWARD CLOCK COMPANY

The venerable Howard Watch and Clock Company was formed in 1881 as a stock corporation, succeeding a number of earlier firms in which Edward Howard had been involved and which had a checkered history, starting in 1842. With the reorganization in 1881, Howard sold his personal interests in the firm and retired. The new management continued to make many of the clock styles of its predecessor firm, mostly weight-driven and of high quality workmanship.

Well established in the market and highly respected, this manufacturer of fine clocks entered electric timekeeping about 1900. The first of their electric masters were simply weight-driven clocks with an electric contact installed to give minute impulses to slave clocks in remote locations, thus following the same practice as many other traditional firms making their first venture into electric timekeeping.

Soon after its initial entry into the electric era, Howard modified an existing movement into an electrically wound type using the same pendulums, cases and styles as their manually wound models. The movements used were of the same plate dimensions as their style #89 with the winding accom-

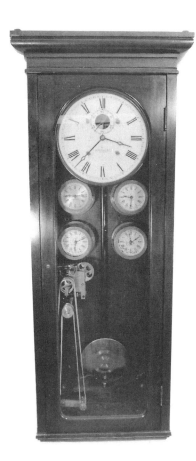
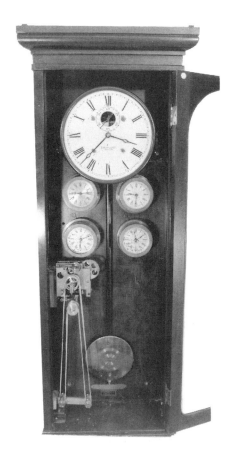

Howard #89 master clock with a 4-track program mechanism and 4 pilot clocks. *Left*, front view. *Right*, door opened to show program mechanism.

plished by an impulse winding arrangement fitted to the movement and the spring being wound on the center arbor.

Howard continued the production of electrically operated master systems until about 1930. The systems could operate almost any number of slave clocks, with the only limitation being the power requirements of the system. The master clock was designed to operate on 24v DC and the remote clocks were wired in series and drew about 5 milliamps each.

There were many modifications made in the program mechanisms and the

systems per se with such things as zone pilot clocks, either in the same or separate cases. Many used a separate relay to operate remotes and carry the winding current. The reason for this is apparent when the contact is examined. They were designed to create as little disturbance to the master clock as possible and were too light for the work. This was true of most such masters and the Howard was no exception.

Unlike most other firms producing program clock systems, Howard never did develop a correction system for their masters. All Howard masters, as with other Howards, are considered quite desirable even though the firm

made no real advances in the science of electric horology.

Suggested Reading

1. Ly, Tran Duy, 1991: *American Clocks*, Volume 2, Fairfax, VA, The Arlington Book Company.

2. Anonymous, 1978: Howard Model 89 Self-Winding Master Clock, *The Journal of Electrical Horology*, October.

3. Anonymous, 1990: Howard Electric Master Clock, *The Journal of Electrical Horology*, March.

Elmer G. Crum, FNAWCC, #33463

Imperial Clock Co

The Imperial Clock Company was started in Granite City, Illinois, a part of the St. Louis metropolitan area, in 1908 by three brothers, Frank, Joseph and August Feraud. All were in the jewelry and watch repair business and Frank got the idea for an electrically wound clock after having a Sempire brought in for repair. The company was incorporated somewhat later by Frank Feraud, John R. Trott and Joseph Steis. At first, the movements were manufactured from start to finish by five workers. Later, finished parts were purchased from other clock companies. Cases were made at a local planing mill and were most commonly wall regulators. Master and secondary (slave) clocks were also made.

The patent (#920,124) for the movement was granted May 4, 1909 and that date appeared on nearly every movement this author has seen, until they introduced their lever escapement version, discussed below. One movement stamped "Patent Applied For" has come to the author's attention which would indicate that the firm was at work prior to being granting their patent.

Although the patented movement has narrow plates, the wider thicker plates of the (presumed) later movements are more common. Both have similar wheel arrangements. The movements were well-made, with stamped and polished verges for a dead beat escapement. The patent electric winding

Wall regulator model with St. Louis address.

Large wall office model with St. Louis address.

mechanism was used in both styles, of course, and did not seem to vary throughout the life of the company. Frank Feraud reportedly felt that his mechanism was superior to that of the Sempire Clock Co., although, on comparison, the reasons for this are not readily apparent. Both movements run well and long with minimal maintenance and they operate similarly, via a

weighted arm lifted electromagnetically by a dry cell battery.

After Imperial was sold in 1910, the firm moved to St. Louis for three years and it was during this period that Imperial is said to have purchased Sempire. All Sempire models were discontinued. For financial reasons a move was made to Kimmswick, Missouri, then back to St. Louis in 1918 after an aborted attempt to move to Rockport, Missouri. Stock had been sold to residents of Rockport and land was donated for a factory. Although the factory was constructed and the name

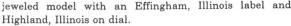

Three office wall models produced in differing locations. *Left,* Highland, Illinois. *Center,* Collinsville, Illinois. *Right,* jeweled model with an Effingham, Illinois label and Highland, Illinois on dial.

of the town was changed to Imperial, no clocks were ever made there.

Apparently the Company had some income from "war orders" during World War I, and shortly after the war they began to manufacture direct current clocks. By 1920, however, Imperial was once again insolvent and it operated for three years under a trustee before being sold to A.W. Fowler and moved to Collinsville, Illinois. A year later, they moved to Highland, Illinois, still in the St. Louis area. From 1922 to 1928, battery clocks were again manufactured. In order to remain competitive, however, Fowler developed and patented an electrically wound clock, still pendulum controlled. Later, he produced movements which incorporated a jeweled lever watch escapement so he could use smaller cases. The escapements originally came from Tavaness in Switzerland, but were later purchased from Waltham and Illinois.

About 1935, Fowler developed and patented striking and Westminster chime mechanisms for use with synchronous motors purchased from Hansen in Princeton, Indiana. At that time he manufactured the smallest full Westminster chime clock on the market.

After World War II, C.J. Hug and his son J.C. Hug bought the firm and changed the name to C.J. Hug Manufacturing Co. Fowler was retained as General Manager and the Imperial name was retained and used on their clocks. Small clocks with synchronous motors, Westminster chimes and the Hug name have been reported and it is

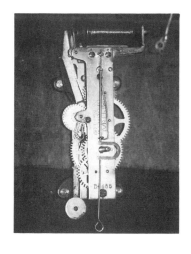

Close-up of Imperial self-winding movement.

Close-up of the jeweled movement in clock on the right above

J.C. Hug miniature tambour Westminster chime model.

stated that Hug continued manufacturing until the late 1960's at the Highland location. It's fate after that time is not known with certainty.

Suggested Reading

1. Tschudy, Robert F., 1958: The Imperial Clock, *NAWCC Bulletin,* VII, 74-76.

2. Hagans, Orville R., (ed), 1979: *The Best of J.E. Coleman: Clockmaker,* Denver, CO, American Watchmaker's Institute Press, 152-153, 320-321, 402-406.

H. Bryan Rogers, FNAWCC #68266

Two J.C. Hug miniature grandfather models.

E. INGRAHAM & CO.

Elias Ingraham, with his son Edward, founded the Elias Ingraham & Company in 1857. The firm, which had several name changes, was incorporated as The E. Ingraham Company in 1884 and became The Ingraham Company in 1958. Elias Ingraham was basically a case maker and had several patents relating to case designs. As a result, movements were purchased from varied sources during the early history of the company and it was not until 1865 that they went into movement manufacture.

Upon Elias' death in 1885, his son Edward succeeded him as head of the company and it was during his term of office that they experienced their greatest growth. A new case shop was built, followed by a new office and movement shop in the early 1900s. By 1932, Ingraham had added a line of inexpensive pocket watches and, later, a line of wrist watches. The manufacture of watches continued until the mid-1960s.

In the early 1930s with the advent of synchronous electric timekeeping and the inroads it was making on sales of traditional spring-driven clocks, Ingraham added electric clocks to its line. It is interesting to note that Arthur B. Poole (son of Arthur F. Poole founder of the Poole Manufacturing Company discussed later in this work) was in charge of the electric clock department of Ingraham from 1931 to 1942 when World War II necessitated that clock manufacture cease. It was during Poole's leadership that the innovative nature of the firm, which was so evident in its introduction of new case types and designs years earlier, continued to be evidenced in its electric clocks. Many contained motors of their own design which were not sealed like those of Warren and others. They could be opened, cleaned and regreased fairly easily.

When electric clocks were first introduced, clockmakers tended to follow the same principles of design that they had followed with spring-driven movements.

Ingraham self-starting office wall clock. (Photo courtesy of Scott Cunningham)

Ingraham Sentinel alarm clock.

Separate power sources were used for both time and strike — two springs, two motors. There were problems here, however, since the strike motor was called on to work intermittently and was maintained in a stalled state the remainder of the time. This was not totally satisfactory because of the heat generated by the motor was not easily dissipated, causing failure of the insulation on the wires and other problems. In 1934, Ingraham claimed to have solved the problem with its unique self-starting synchronous motor strike clocks. Driven by only one motor, the strike mechanism in these clocks was an integral part of the main arbor. According to Jesse Coleman, they worked quite well for 30 years or so and were not too difficult to repair.

During World War II, Ingraham's manufacturing facilities were devoted totally to war production and some of these activities continued after the war when clock and watchmaking resumed. On November 30, 1967, the stockholders of The Ingraham Company sold the business to McGraw-Edison which continued the production of clocks with the Ingraham name at a plant in Laurinburg, North Carolina.

Suggested Reading

1. Hagans, Orville R. (ed), 1979: *The Best of J.E. Coleman: Clockmaker*, Denver, CO, The American Watchmaker's Press.

2. Ingraham, Edward, 1963: More About Poole, *NAWCC Bulletin* XI:54.

3. Bailey, Chris, 1975: *Two Hundred Years of American Clocks & Watches*, Englewood Cliffs, NJ, Prentice-Hall, Inc.

4. Ly, Tran Duy, 1989: *American Clocks: A Guide to Identification and Prices*, Arlington, VA, Arlington Book Company.

William F. Keller #12745

INTERNATIONAL TIME RECORDING CO.

International Time Recording (ITR) was formed in 1900 to buy out the Bundy Manufacturing Company of Binghamton, New York, the first manufacturer of time recorders in the world. ITR, which was to become the International Business Machine Corporation then went on an acquisitions binge for several years, acquiring among other firms several of its competitors in the "time clock business." In mid-year 1901, ITR purchased the Standard Time Stamp Company and later that year, the Willard & Frick firm, manufacturers of the Rochester Time Clock.

Originally, Bundy used large Seth Thomas movements in their clocks and this seems to have carried over to International. According to one source, these were Seth Thomas #88 movements, but #86 movements have also been found in their products. These movements were sold to many firms by Seth Thomas and often modified to fulfill the particular needs of the company using them. They were widely used in program and time clocks because of their accuracy and their durability. To our knowledge nothing but Seth Thomas works were ever used in International's products until they went to electrically powered units. In fact, many of the original spring-driven movements were converted to electric drives using Synchron motors. We have been unable to determine whether these conversions were done by the manufacturer or by local technicians who may have purchased a conversion kit.

Initially, the firm's products continued to be manufactured in Binghamton, the home of Bundy, by 1906 these quarters had been outgrown and ground was broken for a new factory in Endicott, New York designed to house the combined operations. By the time the new plant was occupied the Dey Time Register Company of Syracuse, New York had been acquired and their manufacturing was transferred to the new location.

In June 1911, the parent organization owning International merged ITR with three computing scale firms and a tabulating machine company, all wholly owned, to form The Computing-Tabulation-Recording Company. Initially, the new firm made clocks with "CTR" on

Impulse wound master clock with a drum program mechanism. *Left*, front view. *Right*, door opened to show detail of program mechanism.

Weight-driven master clock with mercury pendulum originally in the Colgate-Palmolive building in Chicago

the dials, but the manufacturer's labels still read International Time Recording. The CTR designation, not to be confused with the "CTR" of Cincinnati Time Recording, was carried only a short time after which the clocks, until 1924, were just labeled "International".

As International called it, electric synchronization of time recorders, a type of program clock system, was introduced in 1919 and a year later ITR began the manufacture of complete program time systems for schools. Introduced early in 1924, the company's self-regulating electric time system was said to ensure "the utmost accuracy and reliability in source time records" and to be the first such system on the market. It was also in 1919 that CTR was reorganized and the International Business Machines Corporation was born. The logo "IBM" was not registered as a trade mark until 1933, however.

Further advances under the aegis of IBM were the first electronic program clock systems and in the 1950s, the

40

IBM synchronous (Telechron) world time clock.

first radio-controlled master clocks commercially available. These clocks received signals from the Naval Observatory twice-a-day and automatically set themselves to the proper time. About five years prior to the sale of its Time Equipment Division to the Simplex Time Recorder Company in 1958, IBM introduced coded signal receivers for timed switching of thermostats, signs and industrial processes.

Suggested Reading

1. Sayles, Alan C., 1961: A Short History of Dial Recorders, *NAWCC Bulletin*, IX:941-942.

2. Auerbach, Louis, 1985: Working Stiffs, *NAWCC Bulletin*, XXVII:190.

3. Harrison Paul, 1979: *The Timekeepers of Business*, Spring Valley, NY, Barry Rosenberg

4. Anonymous, 1936: *Development of International Business Machines Corporation*, NY, New York, International Business Machines Corporation.

William F. Keller, #12745

JAMES REMINDO CLOCK COMPANY

The necessity of meeting schedule times for special customers was the "father" of the invention — the James Remindo Clock. It was in 1933 that Henry James, a cab driver in Monterey, California decided to develop a device to ensure his meeting the schedules set by his trusted customers.

He first attempted to adapt a Westclox alarm clock to his purposes by fitting a metal band around the movement with ties connected to the alarm shaft to provide more than a single signal. This was not too satisfactory, however, since the number of settings was limited by the duration of the wound spring. He then attempted to modify an ordinary electric clock, but finally turned to building his own using a transformer and a Synchron motor. After experimenting with different types of dials and pins he finally developed a model which pleased him and is said to have been the first such clock sold nationally. He called it the James Remindo Clock and a business that was to last for fifty years was launched.

Production was centered in a small factory in Oakland, California and although sales were not high, the firm continued to operate under James' direction until 1963. By that time James was in poor health and the business, including the factory, was sold to Clifford Miller. Miller purchased some new machinery for the plant, increased

the advertising budget, reduced the size of the clock, and designed some new case styles. Featured in the advertising were users such as airlines, hotels, and radio and TV stations. Production rose to 2,000 clocks a year.

By 1973, it was apparent that the Oakland factory was too small and a search was begun for a new location. Miller decided to leave the urban environment of Oakland and settled on the small town of Minden, Nevada where he constructed a new plant and installed machinery and equipment. Production here reached a total of ten units a day on a more compact, smaller model. A variety of new dials and cases were introduced and the clock timers were adopted by several hotel/motel chains.

Miller closed the shop in 1987 after 14 years under his direction. During the lifetime of the firm over 125,000 of the clocks were sold and it would be a wonder if, at some time or other while traveling, one has not been awakened by a call triggered by the clock's alarm.

Suggested Reading

1. Bartels, Joe, 1990: The James Remindo Clock, *NAWCC Bulletin*, 32:125-126.

Joe Bartels, #8514

Early heavy metal cased model with numerous functions: alarm, appliance plug, etc.

Later model with bakelite case.

JEFFERSON ELECTRIC COMPANY

The Jefferson Electric Company was founded in January, 1915 by John C. Daley, John A. Bennan and Arthur R. Johnson and named for our third President, Thomas Jefferson.

The company employed 20 people in their first few months of business and made bell and toy transformers well into the 1920s, when they entered the automotive field. At that point they had about 200 employees and had annual sales of $700,000. Their primary business in 1921 was the manufacture of magneto lamp regulators. By 1924 they were into radio transformers followed by burner ignition transformers in 1925 and neon sign transformers in 1927.

Jefferson purchased 19 acres of land in Bellwood, Illinois in 1931 and constructed a 210,000 square foot building which housed their operation for more than 50 years.

During World War II, Jefferson contracted with the Navy Department to produce transformers for various radar, communications and weapons systems.

Manufacture of their Golden Hour Clocks, often called "Mystery Clocks" because the public did not understand how they operated, began in 1949 after patent rights were purchased from Leendert Prins of the Netherlands. The Jefferson clock was a redesign of the Prins model and a United States patent (#2,642,713) for their design was granted in 1953. The Golden Hour, by

Golden Hour model which was given to Philco television purchasers. Dial diameter is 7 inches.

far the biggest seller among their many models, was offered in gold, bronze and silver with gold being the most popular

by a wide margin. Tremendous advertising benefits were realized from a promotional program of the Philco Corporation which offered a free Golden Hour with the purchase of every television sold in 1953. Over 50,000 clocks were purchased by Philco for that promotion.

Additional clock models, based on Jefferson's original patent were introduced in succeeding years: the Golden Helm in 1951, the Golden Minute in 1955, the Golden View in 1956 and finally the Suspense in 1958. By 1968 over 2

Golden Helm model, 6 inch dial.

Golden Minute model, 6 inch dial.

million Golden Hour models had been sold. Of all the models only the Golden Hour remained in production for any length of time.

Although the Golden Hour clocks, and clocks based on the same patent and principle, were by far the most popular manufactured by Jefferson, they did produce clocks of different designs. Several, made in the early 1960's, were advertised as desk or table clocks, but often called "paper weight" clocks because of their shape and weight. Some of these, such as the Integer, Intermezzo, or the "880" were powered by two

Golden View model, 6 inch dial and 14 inch wide wooden base.

Suspense. Motor is mounted at top and a chain loop hangs over the motor shaft and goes around the dial.

AA batteries and incorporated a novel self-winding system. Others, such as the Lady Marion and the "500" were cased in an identical manner and powered by a 110v, 60c Synchron synchronous motor.

Jefferson was purchased by Litton Industries in 1967 at which time all manufacturing was moved to Athens, Alabama and the firm was renamed MagneTek, Inc. They now produce fluorescent ballasts and a wide variety of transformers. Ironically, this was basically their original product line.

In August 1991, it was announced that MagneTek would no longer produce the Golden Hour Clock or parts for same and that their clock manufacturing division was for sale. Thus ended a most phenomenal sales run of over 40 years for a single clock model. Some repair parts for the Golden Hour can currently be found in parts distributors

catalogs, but when these are gone that will probably be it. Parts and material for all other models are obsolete and unavailable.

Suggested Reading

1. Heffner, Paul V., 1990: The Answer Box, *NAWCC Bulletin*, 32:485-487.

2. Heffner, Paul V.,, 1991: The Answer Box, *NAWCC Bulletin*, 33:327-328.

Steven Berger, FNAWCC, #16873

"Paper weight" clocks. *Left*, the self-winding spring-driven Integer model which is powered by two AA cells. *Right*, Lady Madison model powered by a synchronous motor.

LOWNE CLOCK AND APPLIANCE

Lowne Clock and Appliance was formed in 1903 to manufacture a clock of unique design, invented and patented (British #25374) by Robert M. Lowne. Lowne was born in 1840 and in his 84-year lifetime he secured 18 patents and founded a successful corporation that continues in business today. In 1924, Lowne's sons took over the firm and they now manufacture a wide variety of instruments for numerous industries in the aircraft and scientific fields. The company has been known as Lowne Instruments since 1960.

Lowne was awarded a contract to supply a master clock system to the Royal Arsenal, Woolwich (England) in 1903. The system was to cover a series circuit of over six-and-one-half miles with forty-six slave clocks. Even today, this would be a formidable task, but the system operated satisfactorily for over thirty years when the master clock had to be replaced, although the slaves continued in use. The company continued to manufacture and install clock systems only until 1933, and continued to maintain systems previously installed after that date.

During World War II, the company did work for the Air Ministry and also produced a synchronous clock. After the war they discontinued clock manufacturing as well as maintenance of the few systems remaining after the bombing of England. As a consequence, these clocks are rather rare today, probably existing in the collections of only a few fortunate electric horologists.

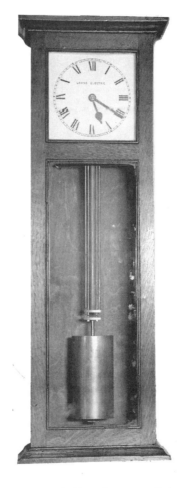

Master clock. Note the unusually large pendulum.

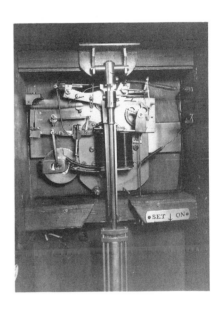

Close-up of movement in clock to left.

Suggested Reading

1. Langman, H.R., and Ball, A., 1927: *Electrical Horology*, London, England, Crosby Lockwood and Son.

2. Aked, Charles K., 1977: *Electrifying Time*, Ticehurst, Sussex, England, The Antiquarian Horological Society.

Elmer G. Crum, FNAWCC, #33463

The movement is quite complicated and one might think it to be the product of someone tinkering in a garage. It was quite expensive to make, but extremely field serviceable, a point often overlooked by other companies.

LUX MANUFACTURING COMPANY

Much has been written about the animated alarms, the pendulettes and the tape-measure clocks produced by the Lux Clock Manufacturing Company, but one finds almost nothing about the electric phase of the firm. What we have assembled here is little more than a brief introduction to this aspect of their operation for it is clearly evident that there were many interesting associations and a great variety of products produced during this time.

Paul Lux, a German immigrant, had been an employee of the Waterbury Clock Company for over 25 years when he founded his company in a small shop in Waterbury, Connecticut in 1912. He was assisted in the new firm by his wife and two sons, Fred and Herman. Just as the company seemed to be succeeding, the factory was destroyed by fire, not an uncommon happening for a clock firm in those days. Then, his sons joined the services in World War I, and in order to keep operating, he had to enlist the help of friends.

Once Herman and Fred returned from the war and rejoined the firm, it entered a period of rapid growth. Not only were pendulettes produced and sold under the Lux name, but in the early thirties they began to make the same or similar clocks for August Keebler, a clock distributor in Chicago. Having two firms selling the same clocks, but under the names of each firm could well account for the numbers of these clocks we see today. In 1935, Henry Lux was granted a patent for the firm's popular tape-measure clock and we mention it here because it is the only basic spring-driven clock that appears to have been produced as an electric clock.

The company was incorporated in 1917, as the Lux Manufacturing Company with a capital of fifty thousand dollars ($50,000.00). Twenty years later, it appears there was a reorganization as the Lux Clock Manufacturing Company with the founder's son, Fred, as President.

Just when Lux first began to produce electric clocks has not been determined. We do know, though, that in addition to producing a line of Lux electrics for the retail trade they also made electric

Silvertone synchronous alarm clock made for Sears Roebuck.

Crawford range timer made by Lux.

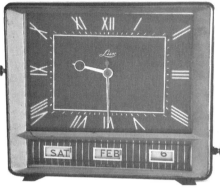

Day-month-date models (circa 1960). *Upper*, wall model. *Lower*, desk or mantle model.

alarms for Sears Roebuck and timers for electric ranges and other appliances. It has also been stated that they may have produced some car clocks, but whether they were electric or spring-driven remains a moot point.

Although Waterbury continued to be their headquarters, the firm built a second factory in Lebanon, Tennessee in the early 1950s. The Robertshaw-Fulton Controls Company took over Lux on an exchange-of-stock basis in 1961. The Lux Products Corporation purchased the Consumer Products Division from Robertshaw in April of 1991 and now operates out of Mount Laurel, New Jersey. That firm produces numerous quartz-timed thermostats which continue to carry the Robertshaw name as well as a line of spring-driven timers similar mechanically to those originally produced by Lux in 1936. The Robertshaw firm continues to

make timers and similar components for appliance manufacturers.

Suggested Reading

1. Burt, Jo, 1981: Lux and Keebler Pendulettes — Fun and Fantasy, *NAWCC Bulletin*, XXIII:335.

2. Desjardins, Rene, 1976: *Clocks with Personality*, Hollywood, CA, Clock Book.

3. Whitmer, Ralph, 1978: Tape Measure Clock, *NAWCC Bulletin*, XX: 286-287.

4. Bailey, Chris H., 1975: *Two Hundred Years of American Clocks and Watches*, Englewood Cliffs, NJ, Prentice-Hall Inc.

William F. Keller, #12745

O.B. MC CLINTOCK COMPANY

Master clock. *Left*, front view. *Right*, door opened to show mechanical Westminster chime movement.

O.B. McClintock came to Minneapolis, Minnesota in 1901 to organize a company to make burglar alarm systems, the American Bank Protection Company. In 1908, with that operation underway, he resigned his position to create the company that was to bear his name, the O.B. McClintock Company, nationally renowned makers of electric chime and clock systems. It is interesting that although McClintock did, on occasion, make tower and street clocks, the major market for the products of both the firms with which he was associated was banks and financial institutions.

McClintock's master clocks were based on modified Seth Thomas #86 movements, possibly provided by Seth Thomas with switches in place. They seem to have built their own cases for the movements.

The earliest models used mechanical tripping for the chime systems, but later models included an electric trip for the hour-chime mechanism. This hour trip was originally a part of the main mechanism but was redesigned, at some point, as a separate mechanism. This might well have been done to reduce the amount of work the base movement had to do.

A very large spring-driven switcher was used to provide the switching for the Westminster chime. It was usually mounted at the bottom of the master case, but in later years it occasionally appeared in a separate case with its own power supply.

The earliest clocks used two sets of wet batteries to operate the master clock, the chimes, and any remote clocks in the system. Only one set of batteries was actually in use at any given time and a switching arrangement allowed the "idle" set to be recharged.

The outside clocks were attractive and artistic with cases of bronze, brass, or copper and came in two-faced and four-faced models, the latter often installed on the corner of a building. The dials were large, usually about 2 feet square. They often featured stained glass and most were back lighted at night. Many of the clocks were custom made and they generally contained a bottom glass with the name of the institution to whose property they were affixed.

Large numbers of the clocks continue in use at this writing, most of them found on banks even though it would appear that none were manufactured after the 1950s. In the early part of the 1900s their distribution was nationwide — from Port Townsend, Washington to Rockland, Maine and from Fort Myers, Florida to Corpus Christi, Texas to San Diego, California. Some have now been moved to shopping centers, but the chime system is generally no longer used since the original master clocks and the chime system had to be hand wound. New masters do not provide for the chimes, only the time mechanism, but are electric and "self-wound" — a concession to the hustle-bustle world of automation.

The chime mechanism is a rather robust device with 5 bell-metal tubular chimes which can range in length from 3 1/2 to nearly 7 feet. The tubes are hung from the top of the outside clocks and are energized by a modified relay device. The match-tuned sets produce a pleasant set of harmonic overtones. The company also produced an interior chiming mechanism similar to one produced by Seth Thomas, but of heavier construction. This was struck by a solenoid device on signal from the same master clock as the outside chime. The interior chime systems are rare and often concealed in the architectural features of the building.

McClintock also manufactured some safe clocks with the timing functions provided by a Seth Thomas #10 movement. The systems were custom made with such levers and switches as were required being added to the basic clocks.

During World War II, the firm engaged in war work making various electric meters (amp, volt, and ohm). In 1948, McClintock bought the Waltham Electric Clock Company from Waltham Watch, partly as a means — we were told — of keeping his loyal female factory workers at work. Thus they began the manufacture of synchronous electric clocks, both timepieces and alarms. Most were sold in jewelry stores and the line included kitchen, mantle, wall, and alarm clocks. They also made movements for a firm in Saint Paul,

O.B. MC CLINTOCK COMPANY

Desk or boudoir clocks. *Left,* wood and brass cased alarm. *Center,* wood cased, brass trimmed timepiece. *Right,* molded celluloid and brass alarm.

Alarm clocks. *Upper,* celluloid and brass case. (Photo courtesy of James B. West) *Lower,* art deco bakelite and brass.

Minnesota which cased and sold them under the name "University".

This venture ended in 1949 when Mc-Clintock was unable to get permission for a price increase from the Office of Price Control. Because of its relatively short history, these clocks are not nearly so plentiful as other synchronous specimens and few are seen on Mart tables. Most are art deco in style and all the author has seen bear patent #2,292,265 on the back even though there may be small differences in their motors.

Except for the above venture in synchronous clocks, the O.B. McClintock firm seems to have been an assembler and adapter of basic clock movements, like so many companies. The author knows of no patents or applications for patents regarding the master clock systems or the associated chime mechanism and has found no patent numbers on any systems examined.

The only references found in regard to McClintock are shown in the Suggested Reading list below. The author has had to rely on his memory of conversations with other collectors and observations of the two-faced McClintock he owns. Any additions or corrections to the foregoing will be appreciated.

Suggested Reading

1. Anonymous, 1917: *Minneapolis Diamond Jubilee*, Minneapolis, Minnesota, Minneapolis Chamber of Commerce.

2. Anonymous, 1943: *Instruction Book — Electrical Tubular Chime and Clock Systems*, Minneapolis, Minnesota, O.B. McClintock Company.

3. West, James B., 1992: The Key Bank Clock of Augusta, Maine, *NAWCC Bulletin*, 34:88-89.

Elmer G. Crum, FNAWCC #33463

MAGNETA CLOCK COMPANY

Magneta electric clocks are unique in that they need no outside source of electricity since they generate their own power. In 1900, when Martin Fischer of Zurich patented his system using a magneto-type of generator, there were continual problems with the battery-powered clocks then available. Primarily they suffered from burned or sticking mechanical contacts and from batteries that were costly and not as reliable as today's. Using a magneto as his power source, Fischer eliminated both concerns.

All of these clocks are recognizable by their massive movements and thick plates. The reasons for this size are

readily apparent when one considers what the movement had to support — between 50 and 100 pounds of weights and a heavy magneto. As one might expect, these clocks had large, tall cases of many variations to fit the particular installation. Master clocks could be purchased either hand-wound or with an electric rewinding system. Remotely operated dials were generally round, of either wood or brass, and from eight to as large as 30 inches in size.

The master clock movement is remontoir driven through a medium-size watch spring that is wound from the main train. The fly escapement that

releases the main train and permits the magneto to cycle one revolution is also operated from the remontoir train. When the main train is released the weights power the magneto through one revolution causing an electric current to be generated. Since the resistance to the rotation of the magneto is determined by the number of remote dials, the need for considerable weight for driving power is evident. The current created by each revolution took one positive and one negative excursion at each release.

For marine use the firm devised a special master clock which would actuate any number of secondary

Chain drive self-winding weight-driven master clock. *Left,* front view. *Right,* doors opened to show winding motor in bottom of case on the right and the Huygens' endless rope principle winding. The two weights weigh a total of approximately 80 pounds.

Strap-driven master clock with one weight. The label reads Landis and Gyr. *Left,* front view. *Right,* doors opened to show the "trigger" which actuates the winding at the bottom of the case.

Close-up of massive movement showing the magento to the left.

Manually wound two-weight master clock.

clocks. A simple device on the master clock permitted all clocks on board a vessel to be corrected simultaneously and many ships were equipped with the system.

Working on these clocks can be dangerous. Extreme caution should be exercised when removing the weights or any part of the associated drive system because of the weight of the parts. Improper removal can cause severe damage to one's hands or feet. Make sure the tape, chain or cable is pinned to prevent unwinding before working on the movement.

Suggested Reading

1. Aked, Charles K., 1977: *Electrifying Time,* Ticehurst, Sussex, England, The Antiquarian Horological Society.

2. Coleman, J.E., 1972: The Answer Box, *NAWCC Bulletin,* XV:520-521.

Elmer G. Crum, FNAWCC, #33463

THOMAS JOHN MURDAY

Thomas John Murday was, by profession, an electrical engineer who became interested in designing and making electric clocks; a typical example of an engineer attempting to apply the principles of his craft to another without being conversant with that area. He is of interest today because his design for an electrically driven horizontal balance wheel clock has a peculiar fascination in its appearance and motion.

While living in Hounslow, Middlesex, England, Murday secured several patents for improvements to electric clocks, but most were already out-of-date because of his lack of understanding of horological principles. Murday's original work was with pendulum clocks which incorporated the already outdated Hipp toggle principle. His designs offered no improvement on those designed by Hipp some 60 years earlier which were clocks of far superior quality. Murday's aim was to reduce the number of working parts in an electric clock to a minimum, but he failed in his efforts since his propulsion system was unduly complicated and delicate. Few of his pendulum clocks have survived since they were never precision timekeepers. Although of primary interest only as a phase in electric clock manufacture, Murday's clocks did incorporate a nickel steel pendulum rod — an indication that he was interested in compensation for temperature changes.

Having made little or no market impact with his pendulum controlled electric clocks, Murday turned to applying his step-by-step propulsion system to a balance wheel clock — a portable electric since none were then available. Once again he employed the out-dated Hipp toggle with an impulsing arrangement from an electromagnet — one of the most inelegant ever employed. The entire design of the clock evidences Murday's ignorance of accepted horologic dictums. As a potential timekeeper, the design was poor yet the clock gave a creditable performance in practice. About 300 of these balance wheel clocks were made and many have survived. They were more expensive than the mechanical clocks available at the time. Because of the attractive motion of the Murday electric clock and the reliability of going, these clocks have proven irresistible to collectors, hence they com-

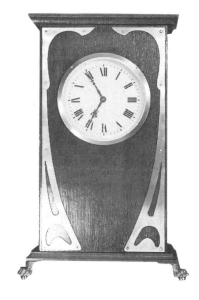 

Wood cased pendulum model. *Left,* front view. *Right,* close-up with door opened to show coils and pendulum at bottom of case.

Large globe balance wheel model.

mand relatively high prices. The most collectable models have glass chapter rings to allow the visual enjoyment of the many individual motions in the propulsion system. These were back painted and the painting has generally deteriorated significantly in the years since 1912 when they were made.

Murday clocks are relatively scarce so few collectors have been able to acquire one the balance wheel models, and the pendulum models are even more scarce. When they do appear, either model should be bought, no matter what the condition.

For those who might be interested in construction, there is presently a series of articles in *The Clockmaker*, published by TEE Publishing, Edwards Centre, Regent St, Hinckley, Leices., LE10 OBB, England; dealing with the making of a Murday style of electrically driven balance wheel clock. A full kit of parts is available for under $100.00.

Suggested Reading

1. Aked, Charles K., 1977: *Conspectus of Electrical Timekeeping,* Ticehurst,Sussex, England, The Antiquarian Horological Society.

2. Aked, Charles K., 1977: *Electrifying Time,* Ticehurst, Sussex, England, The Antiquarian Horological Society.

Charles K. Aked, FNAWCC, #29401

The New Haven Clock Company was formed in 1853 to produce inexpensive brass movements for the Jerome Manufacturing Company. About three years later, after Jerome had gone into bankruptcy, New Haven was able to raise enough money to purchase that firm. Operations were expanded and complete clocks were then manufactured. Sales outlets increased in pace with the manufacturing and by 1880 they had sales offices in Chicago, England and Japan. In addition to their own clocks, they marketed clocks from other domestic manufacturers (Kroeber, Ingraham and Howard) through these outlets and by catalog. This continued for only about five years, by which time New Haven's line had expanded to the point that they had no need for additional items to fill out their catalog.

Westminster chime banjo, Westinghouse powered.

Striking mantle clock. Note the Westinghouse powered notation on the dial.

In 1880, the firm began the manufacture of inexpensive, non-jewelled pocket watches which were essentially a clock movement so small that it could fit into a watch case. Even though they also produced over $500,000 worth of clocks that year and continued to do a sizable business for a number of years, poor financial management (too generous dividends, it has been stated) put them in dire straits by 1890. A change in the presidency did not seem to help much, and by 1894 they were very close to

bankruptcy. Sufficient additional capital was raised to save the firm, however, and it was reorganized three years later.

Walter Camp took over the reins of the firm in 1902 and proceeded to reduce costs by modernizing the watch manufacturing operation, which seemed to be their most successful product line at that point. In 1915, a line of wrist watches was added, to be followed two years later by the first, low-priced jewelled models produced in the United States. A complete line of synchronous electric clocks was introduced in 1930, as well as a successful electric automobile clock. As can be seen from clocks in the exhibit, certain of the electrics carried the notation "Westinghouse" beneath the New Haven name on the dial, evidencing the fact that they purchased at least some of their motors early in the development of their electric line.

During World War II, New Haven worked closely with the U.S. government producing war goods, beginning with a mechanical time-fuse said to have been "used against hostile aircraft." From 1940 through 1946 all clock and watch manufacture was sus-

pended while the company devoted itself totally to the war effort. Included among the products manufactured were anti-aircraft fuses for small bombs, control elements for land mines and units for naval radar.

After the war, the company was reorganized as the New Haven Clock and Watch Company and Swiss watchmaking interests came to control the firm. Although the manufacture of reasonably priced watches and clocks continued until 1956, the company again fell

Early New Haven digital clock.

on hard times and went into bankruptcy. They reorganized, but the end was near. In 1959, after over 100 years of operation, it became clear that the company could not be operated profitably and they ceased operation. The company's assets, including the manufacturing operation, were sold the following spring.

Suggested Reading

1. Bailey, Chris H., 1975: *Two Hundred Years of American Clocks and Watches*, Englewood Cliffs, NJ., Prentice-Hall, Inc.

2. Ly, Tran Duy, 1989: *American Clocks: A Guide to Identification and Prices*, Arlington, VA, Arlington Book Company.

3. Barr, Lockwood, 1957: The New Haven Clock Company, *NAWCC Bulletin*, VIII: 3-12.

William F. Keller, #12745

NEW YORK STANDARD WATCH COMPANY

The New York Standard Watch Company was formed in 1885 in Jersey City, New Jersey and is probably best known for its use of an unusual worm-drive escapement which was discarded after between fifteen and thirty thousand were made. Thereafter, they made fairly normal watches, generally inexpensive jewelled models.

About 1896, they began manufacturing the Fischer Electric Clock invented by Sigismund Fischer in 1895 for which patent #555,313 was granted a year later. Fischer, evidently a rather interesting figure, described himself in 1895 as a subject of the Czar of Russia, residing in Brooklyn. By 1896, he had moved up in the world and was a citizen of the United States.

Fischer's clock, according to his patent, was an "electric clock in which the pendulum is driven by electric impulses imparted to it as from a primary battery, so as to operate a going-train and a striking-train. A recessed block on the crutch of the pendulum is engaged by a pendant (Hipp toggle) pivoted to a fulcrumed level, said pendant engaging the recess of the block when the beats of the pendulum are becoming shorter, so that the lever actuates a circuit closing device, closes the circuit and energizes an electromagnet which attracts an armature attached to the crutch and imparts an impulse to the pendulum. The going-train operates the hour and minute hands, while the teeth on the main wheel of the striking-train serve to close the circuit of an electric bell, so as to strike the full hours. The half-hour striking mechanism is operated by a separate clapper in connection with an eccentric on the arbor of the hour-hand. An alarm device is arranged in connection with the electric clock, said alarm device closing the circuit of the alarm bell at the proper time."

The clocks were noted for their semi-lunar plates and the in-line positioning of the gears. They were sold in well-made cases with 1/2 second to 1 second pendulums, although the 3/4 second was the most common. They could be had without a seconds hand or with either an independent seconds hand or a sweep seconds hand. An early advertisement for the clocks stated that they needed no winding, had no springs to break and no weights to fall. It was

Wall model. (Photo courtesy of Scott Cunningham)

Smaller wall model. *Upper,* front view. *Lower,* view of movement.

Typical NYSWC tall case movement.

said to be so simple and mechanically perfect that repairs were unnecessary and to be self contained with batteries concealed in the clock case and no outside connecting wires. Average battery life was indicated to be from 8 to 10 months with batteries available from any local electric goods dealer for only 18 cents. The clocks were cased in solid woods (oak, cherry and mahogany), had a durable "piano finish," and were advertised as the most accurate of all clocks.

Three additional patents were issued Fischer. The first, #595,911 in 1897, related to a smaller, simplified movement for use in mantle clocks. The second, #603,232 in 1898, related to an improved driving mechanism for the going-train, regulation of the motion of the minute and seconds hands, and synchronization of those hands by a switch operated either by hand or automatically from a master clock whenever said hands arrived at "zero." The final patent, #669,338 in 1901 was for a simplified, and smaller, movement for use in mantle clocks or marine clocks on board ship which did away with the pendulum and was powered by an electrically-wound spring-driven watch movement.

In 1902, the New York Standard Watch Company was sold to the Keystone Watch Case Company. The following year an advertisement in *The Jewelers'* *Circular Weekly* stated that "in order to devote more factory room to the making of N.Y. Standard watches (the demand for which has overtaxed our present facilities), we are obliged to discontinue the manufacture of 'Standard' electric clocks." Thus ended the eight-year manufacturing history of the Standard electric clock.

Suggested Reading

1. Anonymous, 1980: The New York Standard Electric Clock, *Journal of the Electrical Horology Society*, June.

2. Harrold, Michael C., 1984: *American Watchmaking*, NAWCC Supplement No. 14.

3. Ly, Tran Duy, 1989: *American Clocks*, Arlington, VA, Arlington Book Company.

4. Palmer, Brooks, 1950: *The Book of American Clocks*, New York, NY, The Macmillan Company.

5. Burnham, B., 1961: A Battery-Powered Clock, *NAWCC Bulletin*, IX:592-594.

Dr. George Feinstein, #12530

NO-KEY CLOCK CO.

It is doubtful that any clock company had quite as interesting and colorful a history as the No-Key Clock Company. It was organized about 1909 or 1910 as a subsidiary of the Mountain State Electric Company of Wheeling, West Virginia. Their product utilized a principle found in many clocks of that period — a small weight at the end of a lever which "ran" the clock as it descended. When the weight was at the bottom of its descent it closed a circuit between its battery power source and its coils. The resulting magnetic pull of the coils raised the lever and its weight to a "wound" position, and the process started over again.

Just how many clocks may have been made in Wheeling and how successful the firm was in that location is debatable. We do know, however, that Mountain State Electric saw fit to trade the entire business including patent rights, dies, jigs, tools, partly finished

Wheeling, West Virginia model.

clocks and some raw materials (valued collectively at more than $60,000) to a Mr. D.M. Dorsey of Mt. Vernon, Ohio for a coal mine in the Wheeling area that he had inherited. Mr. Dorsey moved the firm to Mt. Vernon, Ohio where he formed a partnership with a Mr. George Owen, a local jeweler. They slightly modified the switch mechanism of the original clock and went into production.

By 1912, several hundred clocks had been made and Mr. Owen, the sales manager of the firm, set out to sell them. His efforts to sell the clocks to jewelers and others for cash were unsuccessful, probably because of the poor reputation most battery clocks had at that time, so he began to put them out on consignment. As was the case with many salesmen in those days, much of his travel was by water. He is said to have followed the Muskingum to Zanesville and Marietta and then to have traveled down the Ohio, stopping at Cincinnati where he consigned what remained of the firm's 1912 production of the No-Key clocks.

Certainly, there were a few of the consigned clocks sold, and in early 1913 replacements were shipped to those consignees who reported sales. The spring of 1913 saw a great flood in Ohio, however, and it has been reported that most of the clocks consigned to these river towns were lost or destroyed in that flood. Suddenly, the firm had no consigned inventory and no stock. They were bankrupt.

An attempt to revitalize the firm was seen in 1914 when a gentleman came to Mt. Vernon, offered to reorganize the firm and guaranteed to go into manufacture and sale of the No-Key clocks for a 51% interest in the firm. He is said to have journeyed to nearby Lodi where he enlisted the help of the Chamber of Commerce in building a new plant and sold stock in the new company to a number of leading businessmen. Subsequently, he established credit at a nearby bank and borrowed $25,000 to buy machinery and other goods, using the firm's patents and the good names of the shareholders as collateral. This took him about six months or so and a few days prior to the scheduled grand opening of the new plant the gentleman disappeared, having withdrawn most of the money in the firm's account.

Once again the No-Key Clock Co. was bankrupt and there was no effort to continue its operation after its very rocky five years of existence.

Suggested Reading

1. Gibbs, J.W., 1971: *Buckeye Horology, A Review of Ohio Clock and Watch Makers*, Columbia, PA, The Art Crafters.

W.F. Keller #12745

POOLE MANUFACTURING CO.

There are nine models of Poole clocks, all are nicely constructed and, if clean and adjusted, they will keep good time. Each will run for a year or more on a new set of three D-size batteries. Their inventor and patentee was Arthur F. Poole, nee 1871, Cumberland, Maryland, the son of a watchmaker. In addition to the patents relating to his clock, Poole also held patents on adding machine features, telephonic equipment and mechanical pencils.

There are inconsistencies as to just when the company actually began, with dates from 1920 to 1924 appearing in the literature. Poole's son, Arthur B., has been quoted as saying that the actual date was 1924 in Westport, Connecticut, but the writer has studied extant clocks and found none with that address. According to some, however, Poole's first clocks were made for the school system of Westport. Just how they came to use a New York City business address is not known, but the earliest specimens seen by this author up to the time of writing have Poole Manufacturing Co., New York City on the dial. Moreover, based on serial numbers and names on the dials, the subsequent chain of addresses (places of manufacture?) for Poole clocks is Morse Chain Company, Ithaca, New York; Morse Products, Incorporated, Ithaca, New York; and Poole Manufacturing Company, Incorporated, Ithaca, New York.

Reliable data have not been found which will allow dates to be associated with the above chain. It is known, however, that the Poole firm move to Ithaca was related in some way to the

funding Arthur received from the Morse Chain Company and that Poole operated independently until 1932 when Morse bought the company. Subsequently, Morse Chain was sold to Borg-Warner, and it has been said that their management's concern about the financial aspects of the Poole operation caused them to close down Poole in 1934.

After several years with the factory lying fallow, through the good services of the Ithaca Chamber of Commerce the plant was cleaned up and, in 1937, purchased by Barr Manufacturing of that city which made typewriters, among other items. They then began the manufacture of clocks based on the Poole design, but with slight differences. Most of their models have no name plate on the base and no serial number, as did the Pooles. Moreover, they have a rectangularly shaped battery case rather than the candle-shaped case found on Pooles and have a differently shaped pendulum. After World War II, Barr produced a line of digital clocks, but for just how long is not known. We do know, though, that the old Poole/Barr plant in Ithaca was sold at auction in 1948.

Early model Poole clocks had porcelainized dials and no seconds beat, while the more often seen later models have silvered dials and a seconds beat. According to one Poole catalog, there were six shelf models available priced from $20 - $35. To the author's knowledge, however, there were also three wall models: one in a banjo case and two in square wood cases. The movements in all models are essentially the same but

Reliance wall model, 14 inches square.

due to mounting modes they are not completely interchangeable. Other differences to be found are: (1) wood or Morsite bases on the Executive #5 model, (2) single or dual electric contacts on various models; (3) the presence or absence of a spirit level and/or serial number on certain clocks, (4) the use of either a type 1 or a type 2 Hipp toggle, (5) the presence or absence of a minute ratchet, and (6) the number of armatures present.

Although there are some who have erroneously called these clocks "gravity clocks," they are actually electro-mechanical with the impulsing arm and roller which drives the pendulum being spring loaded. Jesse Coleman writing in the *NAWCC Bulletin* in 1953 has stated that the mechanism is essentially a remontoire. At intervals, a Hipp toggle mechanism engages causing the armature to drop which in turn impulses the pendulum. Simultaneously, electrical contacts close causing an electromagnet to raise the fallen armature. It remains so poised until trig-

Poole Executive model with glass dome removed. *Left*, front view. *Right*, rear view showing the "regular" candlestick movement.

Salem model.

Patrician model.

Executive model with "winged candlestick" battery case.
Left, front view. *Right*, rear view showing battery case.

Barr Executive model.

gered to fall by the next engagement of the Hipp toggle.

In most clocks with which we are familiar, the clockwork mechanism drives the pendulum, but the reverse is true in the Poole — the pendulum drives the clockwork. For this reason, the bob is much heavier than those found on clocks of comparable size.

The inventor's use of an electro-mechanical device to operate a useful clock was a milestone in American electric horology. Although not rare, there is not an over supply of Poole, or Barr, clocks and one must comb our Marts carefully to find them. Once found and acquired, however, they can be set in running order with relative ease and can provide an intangible pleasure to their owner.

Suggested Reading

1. Grover, V.E., 1953: Poole Gravity-Electric Clock, *NAWCC Bulletin*, 5:502-503.

2. Turner, C.N., 1988: The Poole Electric Clock, *NAWCC Bulletin*, 30:304-310.

3. Bowman, Jr., B.U., 1991: A Brief Report on Poole Clocks, *NAWCCBulletin*, 34:20-23.

Bernard U. Bowman, Jr. #88487

RADIO CORRECTED CLOCKS

The idea of correcting clocks by radio transmitted signals dates from the 1930s. Although radio was in its infancy at that time, it was fast becoming the preferred method of communication. The earliest written information on the use of radio to control clocks, however, is an article, "Radio-Electric Controlled Clocks," by Marius Lavet appeared in *The Horological Journal* of January, 1952.

In the article Lavet based a proposed corrected clock on one that is remarkably similar to those produced by Leon Hatot. The most noticeable difference is the presence of two magnets and two coils, one coil being devoted to driving the pendulum, the other to making corrections via a received radio signal. A very small number of these clocks may have been produced under the ATO label.

With the advent of time signals being transmitted by the National Bureau of Standards on a continuous basis, the possibility of using them to correct clocks in the United States became a reality.

In 1951-1952, Patek Phillippe of Geneva, Switzerland built an "Electronic Timekeeper without any moving parts or electric contacts." This clock used incandescent lamps to indicate the seconds, minutes, and hours on a round dial similar to a standard clock dial, but without hands. The clock was based on a quartz crystal and used hundreds of triode vacuum tubes. It was said to be capable of displaying one-hundredths of a second through the hundred lamps in its outer circle. Whether or not these clocks were ever produced commercially is not known to the author. Mention of them is made

here because of their ability to be corrected by transmissions from stations like WWV.

IBM was the first American company known to make such a clock successfully. It was known as a type 37 and was introduced in 1954. Based on their standard IBM master movement, it had a mass of cams, switches, relays and a radio receiver tuned to WWV. It took the signals from WWV at 10 mgH and converted them into a correction signal for the clock. The movement itself was fitted with an Invar pendulum, the accepted standard for precision clocks at that time. Very modernistic in appearance with all glass doors and a gray finish, the only case style available sported a brushed and painted two-piece dial designed to facilitate servicing with as little disturbance to the clock as possible. After the sale of the IBM clock division to the Simplex Time Recorder Company in 1958, an identical clock was produced under the Simplex name.

Simplex Radio Time. *Upper,* front view. *Lower,* front view with dial removed to show works.

The Zenith Radio Corporation in cooperation with the Hamilton Watch Company introduced what was advertised as "The World's First Portable Secondary Time Standard" in 1959. The standard used a transistor radio tuned to the WWV signal being broadcast from Beltsville, Maryland on any of the frequencies: 2.5, 5.0, or 10 MC. The device was housed in a steel case that was 7x11x7 inches and included a battery weighing 9 pounds.

Hamilton supplied a specially constructed watch movement for the device. According to Hamilton, "The clock's balance wheel operates the set of contacts which pulse the timepiece twice per second. It is waterproof, shock resistant and impervious to extremes of temperature and altitude. It has an opening for visually reading the time, a setting mechanism for adjusting the hour, minute and second hands, a synchronizing mechanism for advancing the second hand, plus terminals for feeding in the power supply and the electrical synchronizing signal from the radio receiver." The clock was powered by a standard 1.5v battery and produced time signals at low cost for many industrial, marine, and government operations needing a portable time standard of high accuracy.

In 1965, the WWV signal format was changed to its present format and these IBM/Simplex models produced prior to then became instantly obsolete since the new format was totally incompatible with the cams used in the old system. It is almost impossible to retrofit the old clocks to the new signal format, as both the frequencies used and the format are different.

Few advances were made in the field until the mid-1970s when Alfred J. Hoehn converted a standard Westclox round wall clock into a WWV corrected clock, sold under the name "Westclox Radio Time" and "Radio Time Services." In 1980, RTS quit the business and clocks were sold under the name "Etaclock" after that time (see paper on Etaclock for more details). These clocks contained a transistor radio receiver tuned to WWV, a specially constructed quartz controlled movement and a small amplifier that would permit listening to WWV. All this caused a correction of the second hand each minute. The hand actually stopped at the 59th second and waited

RTS radio correction modified Westclox wall clock.

for the tone on the minute, basically the same thing as the earlier International and Simplex models. The Hoehn clock is still available directly from him and has recently been technically improved and upgraded. It now has a 60-LED display of the minutes around the circumference of the dial. These clocks are in daily use by the Houston Transportation Department and The Public Transportation Department of New Orleans.

ETAclock model. (Photo courtesy of Dr. A.J. Hoehn)

Until the 1980s most of the users of radio-controlled clocks were television, radio and recording studios, but Heath-Zenith changed all this, making them available to the average consumer. They offered such a clock in kit form which could be easily assembled. It was based on the same radio receiver and interface principles that were in use by IBM/Simplex, but brought up-to-date by use of a digital display clock. This clock kit has been discontinued for some time.

More recently, Junghans, the old respected German clock firm, in cooperation with the LaCrosse McCormick Clock Company, introduced a radio-controlled clock to the American market, some three years after its introduction in Europe. They have secured a trade mark, "Radio Controlled Clock," for this clock which is designed to operate on the lowest frequency radio band at 60kHz, WWVB. This frequency tends to follow the earth's curvature and is, therefore, a very dependable information carrier. After receiving the signals, the clock processes them by a small computer system that operates only at night to correct any daily errors.

The clock is unique in that it displays the day and the date and adjusts for the length of the month including leap years. The clock will also correct automatically for the deletion or addition of leap seconds, if necessary. This feature is provided by taking advantage of the format WWVB transmits and has never been offered on any radio clock system before. The information is displayed on a state-of-the-art LCD.

Junghans also offers a watch version that is available in Europe. *A word of caution!* The format for transmitting time signals in Europe is different than in the United States and a watch or clock purchased *there* WILL NOT WORK *here.* To some degree, the same

Junghans MEGA clock.

warning applies for Canada since their format differs from ours in many areas and some will not permit reception of U.S. time signals.

The Junghans MEGA is advertised as the most accurate clock in the world, and rightly so. It can base its claim of accuracy on receipt of signals from the prime standard that the National Bureau of Standards develops at Fort Collins, Colorado. It is probably the most accurate clock ever produced for the mass market and may portend the way we will keep time in the future.

Suggested Reading

1. Jesperson, J., & Fitz-Randolph, J., 1977: *From Sundials to Atomic Clocks*, (NBS Monograph 155), Washington, DC, U.S. Government Printing Office.

2. Anonymous, 1974: *Time and Frequency: Theory and Fundamentals*, (NBS Monograph 140), Washington,DC, U.S. Department of Commerce.

3. Anonymous, 1990: *Time and Frequency Users Manual*, rev. ed., ed., (NIST Special Publication 559), Washington, DC, U.S. Government Printing Office.

4. Anonymous, 1958: *Simplex Service Manual: Type 37 Clocks*, Gardner, MA, Simplex Clock Company.

5. Anonymous, 1954: *IBM Service Manual: Type 37 Clocks*, New York, NY, International Business Machines Co.

6. Junghans Advertising of 1991-1992.

7. Defossez, L., 1952: Patek, *Journal Suisse Horologerie*, October.

8. Anonymous, 1960 & 1991: Zenith, *American Horologist and Jeweler*, December.

9. Conversations with Dr. Alfred Hoehn.

10. Lavet, Marius, 1952: Radio-Electric Controlled Clocks, *The Horological Journal*, January.

Elmer G. Crum, FNAWCC, #33463

REMPE MANUFACTURING COMPANY

These are rather unusual clocks because of the design of the electric contacts, which were a problem in all self-winding timepieces. The contact is a forced one with a slide motion which tended to be self-cleaning on each winding.

Henry Rempe, a jeweler in Danville, Pennsylvania, was granted two patents: #734,366 (July 21, 1903) and #737,019 (August 25, 1903) relating to electric winding and striking mechanisms for clocks. Most, if not all, of the clocks seen are based on the second patent although some production variants have been seen. The movements were of two sizes, depending on the size case in which they were installed, and both operated on the same principle. They

Mantle model.

were powered by two #6 dry cells, thus operating on 3 volts.

In May, 1903 the company that Rempe had formed with local businessmen (capitalized at $120,000), leased a large brick warehouse building in Danville to begin the manufacture of Rempe's self-winding clock. About six months later the *Jeweler's Circular-Weekly* of November 11, 1903, indicated that the firm was to begin placing its products on the market about November 20 and had hired a number of practical watchmakers from New York. We learn a few weeks later, from a report in the same publication, that there were evidently delays in getting the clocks to market and that shipments "would soon begin." From what can be determined, the Rempe firm was rather short-lived since there is evidence that the company went into trusteeship in late 1904 or early 1905 and probably failed in 1906 or 1907.

Rempe's movement was a fairly simple conventional design with three wheels, two springs and two levers. Its unique feature was the sliding, "self-cleaning" action of the contact point. The shelf model movement was regulated from the front, whereas the wall models were regulated by a rating nut at the bottom of the pendulum.

A 22-page 1904 catalog of the firm shows eight shelf and eight wall models. Most seem to have been darkly stained and according to various sourc-

Modified gallery model.

Mantle model in NAWCC Museum. *Upper*, front view. *Right*, rear view showing movement.

es the cases were made by furniture factories including Muncie Manufacturing Co. and West Branch Novelty Co. of Milton, Pennsylvania and Hoover Brothers, in Danville. All these firms were within a 20-mile radius of Danville.

Rempe advertised very aggressively in the *Jeweler's Circular Weekly* in an effort to meet the competition of the Self-Winding Clock Company which was well-established when Rempe came into the field. Even with their aggressive sales program, however, it does not appear that large numbers of clocks were sold. Certainly, when a Rempe does appear in an occasional Mart, they represent "must buy" for the collector.

Suggested Reading

1. Hanff, Edward A., 1975: Rempe Manufacturing Company; Description of the Clock, *The Journal of Electrical Horology*, November.

2. Wood, Stacy B.C., Jr., 1981: Henry Rempe and the Rempe Manufacturing Co., *NAWCC Bulletin*, XXIII: 264-269.

3. Wood, Stacy B.C., Jr. 1981: Henry Rempe Revisited, *NAWCC Bulletin*, XXIII:527.

4. Personal correspondence, Paul Mc-Williams (Danville, PA) to Paul R. Kloetzly (Tampa, FL), Sept. 24, 1971.

Elmer G. Crum, FNAWCC, #33463

SIGMUND RIEFLER

Sigmund Riefler was born August 9, 1847 at Maria Rain, near Nesselwang, Bavaria. He died in Munich October 21, 1912, at the age of 65. His father, Clemens Riefler, was a scientific instrument maker who founded the firm of Clemens Riefler in 1841. Sigmund studied engineering sciences at a technical high school and then at Munich University. He and his brothers succeeded their father in his business in 1876. The firm was enlarged and moved to Nesselwang, Bavaria where they produced accurately-made, interchangeable drawing instruments for which they became world famous. Fascinated by precision clocks, Sigmund, after twenty years experimentation, produced and patented a new type of escapement embody-

ing a remontoire and giving impulse through the suspension spring. Some early regulators used mercurial compensation, but having noted Professor Thury's work with nickel steel pendulums in 1898, and with the assistance of Dr. Guillaume, he was able to incorporate that type of pendulum in his later regulators.

The step toward the free pendulum with the special escapement impulsed via the pendulum with an electrically-wound movement enabled a barometric cylinder to be used. This eliminated the need to remove the movement for rewinding and made the clock accurate within .01 sec. per day. Riefler's use of the barometric case pointed the way for others and many of the leading obser-

vatories throughout the world installed Riefler precision clocks.

In recognition of his contribution to horological science, a Doctoral degree was conferred on Sigmund Riefler by Munich University in 1897. Other honors followed with the Grand Prix awarded in Paris in 1900, in St. Louis in 1904, in Luttich in 1905 and in Brussels in 1910.

Riefler was a very erudite man with a retiring disposition and a diversity of technical experience. His work pointed the way for further developments in accurate timekeeping. The Cottingham (a Riefler clock installed in Greenwich in 1922) was replaced in 1924 with the William Hamilton Shortt free pendulum which enhanced accuracy to within 10 seconds per year.

As Anthony Randall, FBHI has pointed out (H.J., Jan. 1990, p. 219): "Riefler's escapement seems to have a reputation for excellence for astronomical regulators that is hard to justify on technical grounds. The use of the suspension spring as a remontoir (sic) spring is ingenious, economical, and simple. On the other hand it employs two scape (sic) wheels and double set of pallets — which is not. The worst feature is that the moment of interchange of the pallets is inevitably governed to a greater or lesser extent by the state of friction on the locking pallets, whether or not they are oiled. The speed of rewinding, and with it the impulse, is also dependent on the state of oil on the lifting pallets, and in the clock generally. Errors of gearing also play a role. These shortcomings are confirmed by the fact that many Rieflers, including the one at Greenwich, have a train remontoir (sic) on the third arbor. If a so-called constant force escapement requires a train remontoir to give it stability, is this not an admission of defeat?"

Suggested Reading

1. Riefler, Dieter, 1951: *Riefler — Prazisionspendeluhren 1890 - 1965*, 151 pages. Includes portraits of Sigmund and Clemens Riefler, factory photographs and details of the clocks produced.

2. Rawlings, A.L., 1948: *The Science of Clocks and Watches*, 2nd ed., London, Pitman Publishing.

3. Riefler, Dr. Sigmund, 1907: *Präzisions-Pendeluhren und Zeitdienstan lugen für Sternwarten*, Munich, Theodor Ackerman.

Dr. F.G.A. Shenton #24861

SANGAMO ELECTRIC COMPANY

The Sangamo Clock Company and the Illinois Watch Company were deeply intertwined. Jacob Bunn, who was appointed President of Illinois in 1877, was a central figure in the histories of both firms. In 1899, he was intrigued by a motor developed by a German engineer, Ludwig Gutmann, and the Sangamo Meter Company was formed as a result of his interest. Under Bunn's direction the satellite company flourished. More than 4,000,000 meters were sold to utility companies. Sangamo also manufactured radio parts and other precision instruments and the Sangamo Engineering Research Laboratory had an international reputation.

Fred Holtz, an engineer at Sangamo, approached Bunn in 1924 with the idea of using one of their meter motors to wind the mainspring of a clock. Even though battery-wound and electrically-driven clocks had been introduced some years before, there were problems with them — electric current frequencies were not consistent causing problems with synchronous electric clocks and bad contacts and battery failures plagued the battery models. Consequently, they did not gain wide acceptance and were considered unreliable. Holtz' concept of using Sangamo's successful motor with a high-grade watch escapement to control the power of the mainspring appealed to Bunn. He gave Holtz permission to investigate the concept and develop a prototype. A

Self-winding crystal regulator with glass front, sides and back. Said to have been used as a salesman's sample.

clock utilizing the Sangamo motor, an Illinois watch escapement, a mainspring and an ingenious braking device to prevent overwinding the mainspring was soon made.

The decision to manufacture was reached and market research begun. Gold-plated precision-type gearing, staffs and pinions made of highly polished carbon steel and the finest mainsprings available were used.

Further market testing was done in 1924 when approximately 40 prototype clocks were assembled and distributed to Sangamo engineers and some large jewelry stores to observe their efficiency and accuracy. So encouraging were the results that a decision was made to tool up and begin manufacture.

The first "factory" clocks were produced in the spring of 1926 for delivery to the

Boudoir model.

market in October of that year. During this period, decisions were reached on how to house the clocks. In light of the high quality of the movements, it was decided that the cases should be of similar quality. The Erskine-Danforth Co. (also called Danersk) and the Gorham Co. (of Gorham Silver), both in Connecticut, were selected to produce

Three mantle models. *Left*, synchronous. *Center*, self-winding. *Right*, synchronous.

the wood and bronze cases, respectively. Custom-made cases in different materials, shapes and designs were also produced.

Two series of clocks were produced, the "7 Series" which had 7-jewel escapement and the "11 Series" with an 11-jewel double roller escapement. Early models had separate motors for time and strike, but later both were driven by one motor. An interesting feature of the standard motors was their ability to run on currents from 80 to 130 volts and from 50 to 125 cycles, thus overcoming the vagaries of the unstable currents of the times and keeping time within their guaranteed accuracy of 30 seconds per day. For those in areas with direct current or 220 volts AC, Sangamo supplied rectifiers, or slightly different motors. Performance of the clocks was guaranteed for two years and all were Underwriter Approved and Bureau of Standards verified. The Grand Prix of the Sesquicentennial Exposition in 1927 was awarded to Sangamo for their electrically-wound clocks.

The clocks had many advantages over the other electric and battery-powered clocks of the period. There were no contact problems, no brush replacements, no problems with power failures, no dead batteries, and since no pendulum was involved, getting the movement in beat was unnecessary. Moreover, the mainspring was said to be kept wound to a continually uniform tension, thus eliminating the power variations prevalent in key-wound clocks. The clocks were produced for only five years, but one must wonder how long a company offering such a

Mantle model.

guarantee and such claims could remain in business competitively, even in those days.

Since all the components of the clocks were of high quality, they were relatively expensive for the times in which they were produced. The cheapest 7-jewel clock sold for $25.00 and the basic 7-jewel time-and-strike tambour sold for $40.00; this during a period when the average salary was only about $25.00 per week. Many of the cases made by Erskine-Danforth were copies of famous American and English clocks, made of fine-grain rare woods, such as burled walnut and crotch mahogany, all rubbed to a dusky richness. Perhaps the most famous and most desired is the Act of Parliament model, followed by the Willard banjo style case. Grandmother and Grandfather styles

Banjo in case probably made to order.

with Westminster chimes were also produced.

The Illinois Watch Company and the Sangamo Clock Company were purchased by Hamilton in 1928 and the clock segment of the purchase was renamed the Hamilton Sangamo Clock Company. The standard elliptical Sangamo logo found on dials of the original firm was replaced by Hamilton Sangamo and the Illinois escapements were replaced with Hamilton models.

Self-winding tambour model with visible escapement. (Photo courtesy of Bill Ellison)

Wall model synchronous.

Shortly after the purchase by Hamilton, electric generating companies began to supply more consistent power. Synchronous motors were also improved and there was a proliferation of cheaper electric clocks in the market. Hamilton developed its own synchronous motor which required that a lever be pushed to initiate motor rotation. These were placed in the wood tambour cases and newly developed novelty cases. These movements would operate properly on 110 to 125 volts/60 cycles only and any fluctuation in power would cause them to stop thus negating the reliability reputation previously established with the main-spring movements and limiting the market to those areas where power specifications were consistent with the limits of the motors.

It has been indicated that Sangamo had plans for a Master clock system for use in commercial buildings, but whether the plan was ever implemented is not known.

The General Time Instruments Corporation of New York, a holding company owning Westclox and Seth Thomas,

purchased the Hamilton-Sangamo Corporation in 1931. Sangamo motors were then used in Westclox electric clocks and Sangamo movements, with many variations, were incorporated in Seth Thomas Clocks. One such clock was appropriately called "The Sangamo." General Time continued to produce synchronous motor clocks, but dropped the Hamilton name on the dials and substituted "Sangamo" in initial caps. The rectangular copper plate affixed to the back of the clocks reads "Sangamo Clock Co., Thomaston, Conn.," reflecting Seth Thomas' involvement.

Hamilton-Sangamo art deco synchronous desk model. Ebonized wood with cast metal sides.

Hamilton-Sangamo wall model.

Hamilton-Sangamo miniature tambour.

Suggested Reading

1. Hagans, Orville R., (ed), 1979: *The Best of J.E. Coleman: Clockmaker*, Denver, CO, American Watchmaker Institute Press.

2. Lanphier, Robert C.,: *Forty Years of Sangamo*, Springfield, IL, Privately published.

Stephen Longo, #6602

Hamilton-Sangamo synchronous banjo.

Hamilton-Sangamo synchronous pillared gothic mantle.

SCOTT CLOCK

Herbert Scott of Bradford, England was 37 years old when he was granted a patent (#10271) for his electrically-operated clock, but it was several years later before the clock was produced commercially. After some searching, he convinced the Ever-Ready Electric Specialties Company to produce clocks using his design and patent.

The clocks were made in only three designs: a glass domed model, a mirrored-back glass and wood crystal regulator model and a similar model with a drawer in the base to hold the batteries. All of these clocks are rare and to be found in only a few electric collections.

Scott clock with unusual "to-fro" pendulum movement. Battery chambers are the round columns on either side.

The design of the clock was unique in that the pendulum swings from front-to-back rather than from side-to-side, as do most pendulums. Its uniqueness, however, did not keep it from the same contact problems that plagued other battery electrics.

Manufacture of the Scott-patent clocks ceased in 1912.

Suggested Reading

1. Shenton, Alan & Shenton, Rita, 1985: *The Price Guide to Collectable Clocks*, London, England, Antiques Collectors Club.

Elmer G. Crum, FNAWCC, #33463

Self Winding Clock Company

There are probably few people over age 40 who are not familiar with, or have at least seen, one or another model of a Self-Winding clock. Certainly, until the relative demise of Western Union Telegraph Company in the early '60s, they could be seen in the window of almost any of their offices. Although many called them "Western Union" clocks, they were made by Self-Winding and often remained their property, having been leased or rented by the user. These were but one of the numerous models the firm made, however, and their 1908 catalog included tower clocks, program clocks, office regulators and some models for the home.

Self-Winding had its genesis in 1886 in New York City when Charles Pratt, its first President, and Henry Pond joined together to manufacture and sell an electro-mechanical clock patented by Pond (#308,521) in 1884 and an improved version patented in 1887. Although Pond remained an active member of the management of the firm for only four years, his contributions to the areas of telegraphy and timekeeping continued for many years after his retirement.

The basic principle of the Self-Winding clock was to employ only a small portion of the clock's mainspring, rewound on an hourly basis by an internal mechanism. This would provide more uniform power to the

Model #9 with mercury pendulum.

clock and eliminate the manual winding requirement altogether.

The firm's 1887 catalog offered twenty-six models including mantle and wall

clocks, all priced considerably higher than similar weight or spring-driven clocks. During the early years, most of the basic movements and cases were made by others, with Seth Thomas and Howard being the predominant suppliers. The purchased movements were modified in Self-Winding's plant, where winding mechanisms and other attachments were added. Later, the company moved to a new and expanded plant in Brooklyn which allowed them to manufacture the entire movement.

By 1908, the Self-Winding firm had issued a 146-page catalog offering clocks of all descriptions, including tower clocks, post clocks, watchman's time detectors, fully jewelled astronomical regulators and program devices that allowed for the installation of a customized bell-ringing system for schoolroom or factory use.

With the growth of the railroads in the late 1800's, Pond sensed the need for a national system of time distribution which would allow the railroads to develop schedules on a national basis and would permit other businesses to set meaningful hours nationwide. Although, there had been a number of systems proposed that permitted all clocks within a school or office to be synchronized, none of these had an individual correcting feature and most required that their spring-driven movement be wound weekly. However, one system devised by Gardner, provided

train stations and other users requiring accurate time.

The inestimatable advertising value of the "Naval Observatory Time" clocks in store windows and Western Union offices assisted in the profitability of the organization well into the era of inexpensive, accurate synchronous motor clocks which had replaced virtually every other type of timekeeper for home and business use.

The firm reached its peak prior to World War II and business declined until they discontinued operations in the late '60s, finally closing their NY office about 1970.

Wall model with "A" type movement #395. *Left*, front view. *Right*, close-up of movement.

Metal cased Western union model (circa 1955).

for a signal sent at one-minute intervals to a group of remotely located secondary, or slave, clocks. Its disadvantage was that the clocks would stop in the absence of the synchronizing signal, or without weekly winding. It was almost inevitable that Pond's automatic rewind system and Gardner's concept of remote synchronization be combined. Tests of the new combined system in Chicago, utilizing telegraph lines to send the signals, were so successful that Pond purchased Gardner's patents and began making Self-Winding clocks with synchronizing capabilities available.

In 1889, Pond was issued patent #408, 846 for "An Automatic Time Signaling Device for Time Service." This patent was the cornerstone on which Self-Winding was able to develop a plan for the distribution of correct time with the Western Union Time Service Group, utilizing telegraph lines to transmit hourly time signals from the Naval Observatory in Washington, DC. The partnership was a long and valuable one for both organizations. Self-Winding provided clocks and performed such maintenance as was required at the factory. Western Union installed and adjusted the clocks along with

Dome covered striking mantle model. *Upper*, front view with dome removed. *Lower*, back view showing movement.

replacing the batteries and such field repairs as were required. Western Union provided the wiring for the synchronizing signals, and the partnership benefitted from the rental of the equipment to offices, factories, bus and

Suggested Reading

1. Ly, Tran Duy, 1991: *American Clocks*, Volume 2, Fairfax, VA, The Arlington Book Company.

2. Goodrich, Ward L., 1905: *The Modern Clock*, Chicago, IL, Hazlitt & Walter, Publishers.

3. 1983: The Self-Winding Clock Company, *The Journal of Electrical Horology*, June.

Martin Swetsky, FNAWCC #31665

SEMPIRE CLOCK COMPANY

From a very brief news item in the *Jeweler's Circular* of June 9, 1897 it is known that the Sempire Clock Company was incorporated in St. Louis, Missouri on June 1 of that year, with Bernard Ryan, Henry Rhorer and Frank E. Ryan as the principals and only stockholders. Nothing more is known about these gentlemen.

On the plates of all Sempire movements seen by the author is stamped the name F.L. Gregory, along with two patent dates: July 7, 1891 and Jan. 2, 1894; and the abbreviation, "PAT." Some information regarding this gentleman has been gleaned from St. Louis city and business directories. In conjunction with examination of patents granted to him, a few suppositions may be made regarding Gregory and his relationship with Sempire to complement beliefs traditionally held by horologists. However, in truth, more questions have been generated than answered in the mind of this author.

Frederick L. Gregory's name first appears in the St. Louis directories in 1893 along with a local address and the single word "Electric." He is not mentioned again until 1898 when he is listed as "Supt., Empire Clock Co." (a

Typical Gregory patent movement from a Sempire regulator model.

typographical error) with no address. The Sempire Clock Co., 423 N. 4th appears for the first time in 1898. Gregory is not listed independently again, but Sempire is listed annually at many different addresses, and in progressively smaller type until 1908. The Imperial Clock Co. first appears in 1910, coincident with the reported takeover of Sempire by Imperial, and following Imperial's move from Granite City, Illinois to St. Louis.

Patents issued to Mr. Gregory tell a somewhat different, and at times confusing, even contradictory, story. Those of July 7, 1891 and Jan. 2, 1894 describe the two movements which appear in every Sempire clock seen by the author, and all the movements are stamped alike without regard to the obvious differences between them. However, Gregory is shown as residing in Niagara Falls, New York at the time of their issuance, and the two dates bracket his first listing in a St. Louis city directory. His name and a third patent date of May 2, 1893 appear on the armature of the electric-winding mechanism. A copy of this patent could not be located, but the date may offer a clue to Gregory's first appearance on the St. Louis business scene.

The remainder of his patents, all pertaining to improvements to his electric clock movement (including several striking mechanisms), were issued from

1894 to 1901. They all identify him as a resident of Chicago, and the last one, dated March 26, 1901, is assigned "to the Sempire Clock Company, of the same place."

Discrepancies are obvious in any attempt to rectify information gathered from these sources, and many questions arise. Questions which remain unanswered in the opinion of this author. Further study is needed, along with a careful horologic and electromechanical assessment of the many patents issued to the elusive Gregory. Details of his life are also missing and deserve additional research.

The Sempire movements are all well-made with sturdy brass plates and wheels, cut steel pinions and arbors, and hardened steel verges for dead beat escapements. All have seconds bits or sweep second hands. The patent electrical winding mechanism is very dependable and has been analyzed by Ellison from an electrical and mechanical perspective.

Sempire (St. Louis) grandfather. (Photo courtesy of Dave Miller)

School house model #9.

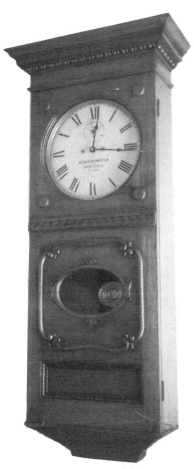

Special order wall vestibule model, 4 feet high. (Photo courtesy of Steve Cunningham)

Wall gallery, 30 inches square. (Photo courtesy of Steve Cunningham)

Mantle model.

The cases are also well-made, most of solid wood, and most finely finished. Cut glass jar mercury pondulums are seen on many models.

The word "Electrometer" appears on the dials of almost all models seen by the author, but its meaning is unknown. It may be assumed that it represents nothing more complicated than a means to promote sales.

A two-page catalog dated 1904 is extant, but it shows only wall models, all named, as well as a price list and other advertising. Reprints have appeared in two recent publications (see 3 and 4 below). The catalog is not all-inclusive, as many other models have been seen and reported, including very small shelf clocks and exceptionally large grandfather or hall clocks. Included in the catalog is a rather lengthy, but interesting, testimonial to the accuracy and dependability of Sempire clocks by "A. Ramel, Ass't in Charge, Washington University (St. Louis) Observatory."

Suggested Reading

1. Anonymous, 1897: Sempire Clock Company, *Jeweler's Circular*, June 9.

2. Ellison, William, 1988: Sempire Clock Company (Electrometers); Operation of the Electric Switch, *The Journal of Electrical Horology*, December.

3. Anonymous, 1981: Sempire Clock Company (Electrometers); Advertising and Prices, *The Journal of Electrical Horology*, December.

4. Ly Tran Duy, 1991: *American Clocks*, Volume 2, Fairfax, VA, Arlington Book Company.

H. Bryan Rogers, FNAWCC, #68266

The Sessions Clock Company

The Sessions Clock Company might well be said to have risen from the ashes of the E.N. Welch Manufacturing Co. which was, in the second half of the 19th century, Bristol, Connecticut's largest clock manufacturer. The Welch firm had experienced two devastating fires in 1899. Although they replaced the factory buildings that were destroyed, they were not able to survive this additional blow to their already troubled financial situation. By 1902, when the demise of Welch was clearly evident, Session family members owned significant amounts of Welch stock and some served on the firm's Board.

The Sessions had numerous investments in Bristol and owned established

trunk hardware and foundry businesses. When the Welch firm went into receivership in 1902, Sessions' interests, for all intents, controlled the firm and William E. Sessions was elected President of the E.N. Welch Manufacturing Company. By July, 1905, three members of the Sessions family had increased their holdings to the point that they owned all of the preferred, and all but 40 shares of the common stock.

On January 9, 1903 the name of the firm was officially changed from the E.N. Welch Manufacturing Company to the Sessions Clock Company. William E. Sessions continued as President and Albert L. Sessions, nephew of William,

was Vice-President. By 1907, the firm had been financially revitalized, the factory expanded and they were producing over half-a-million clocks a year.

With the advent of consistent electric power and the increasing interest in electric timekeeping, the company began experimenting with alternating current electric movements in 1928 and shipped its first electrically-powered clocks in 1930. These were timepieces, though six months later a Westminster chime model was offered. Initially, Sessions made its own basic electric clock movement and powered it with motors purchased from Hammond. A year or so later, they introduced clocks with electric motors of their own manu-

Manual-start Westminster chime tambour. Motor is started by turning second hand.

Self-start desk model.

facture which were of low quality, very noisy and unreliable. Many clocks were returned because of these motors. Sessions then reengineered and improved them until they were reliable.

Almost 40,000 electric clocks were manufactured in 1930, about 13% of their total production that year. Ten years later, over 90% of their total production of 707,656 was electric clocks. During 1942, the company received some small contracts for defense work and clock work ceased late in that year. The only clocks produced during the war were a short run of "Regulators" made for the Army, the last of that popular model produced by the firm. After World War II, the company no longer manufactured spring-driven pendulum clocks, and turned production totally to electric clocks, offering a wide selection of models.

In the early 1950s, business started to decline and the firm began to borrow heavily. One notable model produced in 1955 was "The Lady". This unusual clock was designed to predict the days of greatest fertility and least fertility in a woman's menstrual cycle when properly set. Acclaimed as the first family planning clock, it evidently was not too popular since it was not offered in subsequent years and few appear in Marts.

By the mid-1950s the company had been unionized and had ever increasing financial problems. One of their creditors, Consolidated Electronics Industries Corporation of Wilmington, had an option to buy Sessions by January, 1957. It exercised this option during 1958 and purchased controlling interest. Even though business did improve slightly during the early 1960s, financial problems continued.

Manual-start bakelite mantle model.

Novelty advertising clock with self-start Sessions movement.

Coin operated hotel alarm with Sessions self-start movement.

An employee strike following the failure of union negotiations caused Consolidated Electronics to dispose of the firm, selling the clockmaking division to United Metal Goods Manufacturing Company of Brooklyn, New York. It was the intent of the remaining company to expand its production of timing and control devices, but the financial situation allowed for little expansion. In 1969, they merged with North American Phillips (Norelco), but this was of no help and the Sessions factory was closed about nine months later in May, 1970.

Suggested Reading

1. Bailey, Chris H., 1977: *Sessions Clocks, Catalog #65, 1915* (Reprint), Bristol, CN, American Clock and Watch Museum, Inc.

2. Bailey, Chris H., 1977: The End of An Era: The Sessions Clock Company, *NAWCC Bulletin*, XX:583-597.

Chris H. Bailey, FNAWCC #19100

SETH THOMAS CLOCK CO.

The Seth Thomas Clock Company began in 1913 when Thomas, after several years experience in clock-making with Eli Terry, Silas Hoadley and others, purchased the Heman Clark operation. Early on, the firm manufactured tall case clocks with wooden works similar to those Thomas had built with Hoadley. Later, they also made cast brass movements building on the experience of the Clark employees who were making this type movement when the factory was purchased.

By the time the Seth Thomas Clock Company entered the field of electric horology they were well established in the time business and probably had some experience in electrical work from their association with the Self-Winding Clock Co, beginning about 1890. Also by that time, many other firms had adapted their basic movements for use in electrically-wound and master clock systems.

In 1922, they made their first electric secondary clocks which carried no model number designation. That same year a large, self-winding electric master clock movement also appeared in their catalog. These were in cases from their existing line and the movement appears to be a modification of their #61A, which first appeared in 1904, with contacts and coils added for winding.

Although originally designed for spring-driven clocks, the Seth Thomas movement #86 was widely used as the basic movement by many "electric"

Sharp gothic synchronous mantle clock.

companies such as Self-Winding, Mc-Clintock, International Time Recording, Frick and others. Probably the first use of this large movement, however, was in its spring-driven version by the Southern Calendar Clock Company in their "Fashion" models in 1877. By 1924, moreover, the company had developed and cataloged its own modification (#86AF), a electrically restored ladder style self-winding movement. It is doubtful that any movement ever produced had as many variations and was used in as many different ways as this large heavy movement, which could be supplied with hour and half-hour striking.

All electric appliance timer.

Mantle model with drawer beneath movement.

Rhythm model with strike.

Seth Thomas introduced its first electric motor clocks in 1928, using a special motor to wind the spring. The design allowed the motor armature to be stalled inordinately without harm. A General Electric motor was used to wind the mainspring until a counter torque, acting downward on the motor shaft, depressed the shaft and caused the rotor to strike a stationary brake. Mainspring tension was said to be constantly maintained through the action of the brake. This movement is found in cases of many styles and was used until the late 1940s.

Even as they continued to produce the electrically-wound clocks described above, Seth Thomas began manufacturing synchronous motor clocks in the late 1920s. The motors were of their own peculiar "open" design and they continued to use them in their clocks for many years. With the advent and popularity of the Bulova Accutron watch, the company in cooperation with the Jeco company in Japan developed a tuning fork clock, the Acrotyne. Production of the movement was rather short lived because of the development of quartz movements.

Although Seth Thomas died in 1859, he had organized his business as a stock corporation some years before his death and his sons managed the firm until 1931, when it became part of the General Time Instrument Corporation.

Suggested Reading

1. Sangster, John R., 1968: Seth Thomas, A Yankee Clockmaker, Chapter 3, The Seth Thomas Clock Company, 1853-1900, *NAWCC Bulletin*, XIII:533-545.

2. Ly, Tran Duy, 1985: *Seth Thomas Clocks and Movements*, Arlington, VA, Arlington Book Company.

Elmer G. Crum, FNAWCC, #33463

Electrically restored ladder-type self-winding movement.

Sohm Electric Clock Company

As with a large number of early clock companies, information on the history and the principals of the Sohm Electric Clock Company is difficult to find. We must suspect that little was ever recorded or, that what was recorded, was destroyed when the firm was dissolved.

We do know, however, that at least eleven patents were issued to Alfred I. Sohm during the period from 1912-1922. Most relate to clocks and clock mechanisms, particularly master clock systems. The first patent, of which we have record was #1,049,004 for a secondary clock. Seven more patents were granted him between 1915 and 1921 for such things as a "time-controlled electrical contact mechanism," and a secondary clock system. All were assigned to the Sohm Electric Clock Company, so it would appear that the firm was largely involved in the business of making master clocks systems during its early history. Just how many may have been made and sold is not known.

There is clear evidence through advertisements in *The Jewelers' Circular Keystone*, nonetheless, that the firm was located at 849 Blue Island Ave. in Chicago in early 1922. Whether this was their original location and when they were actually established has not been determined. Most of their advertising during this period was directed at jewelers, rather than at the ultimate consumer, and they appear to have offered a full line of commercial clocks in a variety of cases and finishes. These clocks, advertised as "The Clock That Requires No Winding," seem to have been based on Sohm's patents #1,394,689 and #1,418,487 for a self-winding and a "keyless" clock, respectively, issued in 1921 and 1922. To quote further from the advertising: "He (evidently meaning Sohm) knows the public demand and is acceding to it. He is not trying to sell key-wound clocks, any more than the automobile dealer is trying to sell the old hand-cranked car."

According to their catalog, their self-winding clocks were provided with either an 80- or 120-beat movement, powered by two #6 dry cells which were said to last for from 12 to 18 months. Housed in cases said to be dustproof(?) and hand finished, the clocks were not

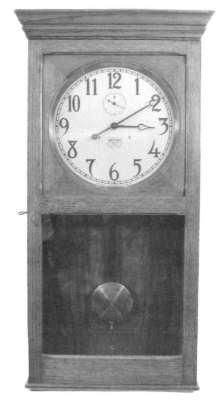

Regulator model. *Upper*, front view. *Lower*, close-up of unique movement.

inexpensive for that period. An 80-beat regulator said "to have ample space on the front for advertising purposes," sold for $21.00 wholesale. They were sold with a money-back guarantee, but no mention is found of the length of that guarantee. The company also offered a liberal (6%) discount if their invoice was paid by cash within 10 days — rather aggressive marketing even for 1922.

Later advertising from the same year offered a cooperative sales program. One must wonder if all this might have been an indication that trouble was brewing for they moved to another location on Blue Island Avenue that year and, from the small number of clocks that appear today, it would seem they must have been in business for only a relatively short time, perhaps ten years at the most judging by the patent assignment dates.

The clock most often seen is their #240, an 80-beat oak regulator style, although there are other styles extant. The unique design of the clock's movement warrants collectability. This author's experience with a number of Sohm clocks indicates that they are rather troublesome because of their silver contacts. These oxidize rapidly, arc suppression is non-existent, and unreliable winding is a constant problem. The clocks seem to require continual maintenance and this might well account for the short life of the company. The cases are well constructed and remind one of those housing Automatic and American Clock Company products, both Chicago firms, suggesting the possibility that the same case maker may have supplied both companies.

From reviewing Alfred Sohm's patents and what little data that are available, it would seem that this is a company, and a man, that could deserve further research. Basically, the clocks are well made and are most interesting.

Suggested Reading

1. Anonymous, 1922: Sohm Electric Clock Company advertising, *The Jewelers' Circular Keystone*, February and April.

Elmer G. Crum, FNAWCC, #33463

SPARTUS

Spartus began operations in Chicago, Illinois in the late 1940s and for some 20 years operated under a variety of names including Galter Products and Herold Products Company. Initially, the product line included a variety of products: cameras, electric shavers, and key-wound and synchronous clocks among them. As early as 1950, Galter Products was involved in the manufacture of synchronous clocks using a manual-start motor.

In 1954, the company acquired the rights to a Westinghouse patented self-starting hysteresis type electric motor, paying the patentee a royalty for its use. Unfortunately, the motor, as designed and patented, was too large for the clocks in which Galter wished to use it. Allan Gold, an electrical engineer, was hired to redesign the motor and develop a gear train suitable for use in a wall clock they wished to produce. Although the newly designed motor was never patented, it became the Spartus "58" movement which, with only minor modifications, was used in all Spartus clocks until synchronous movement manufacture ceased.

The firm officially became Spartus in 1960 and clock production began to increase. Seeking a more favorable climate for growth, Spartus moved its entire manufacturing operation from Chicago to Louisville, Mississippi in 1963 and continued to manufacture most of the items produced in Chicago. At this writing, the firm occupies one of the largest buildings in Mississippi with almost 13 acres under one roof.

Spartus bought the name, equipment and manufacturing rights for the Gilbert clock line from the William L. Gilbert Clock Company in 1965 and the Spartus clock line was thus expanded to include key-wound and electric alarm clocks. Unfortunately, the Gilbert synchronous motor, while smaller than that designed by Spartus, was of an inductor permanent-magnet rotor design and did not lend itself to the animation of many Spartus clocks. As a result, it saw only limited service in the short-lived electric alarm clock line which was dropped by 1970. It was during the late 1960s, also, that the company began to produce battery clocks using balance wheel movements purchased from General Time Corporation and others.

"Plate" model kitchen clock. Herold Products label.

Kitchen model. Herold Products label.

Recent vintage digital alarm.

Walter Heller & Company purchased Spartus in 1966 and, in 1969, a controlling interest was purchased by Walter Kidde & Company. Then, in 1970, the firm became a division of the LCA Corporation. By the time of the LCA purchase in 1970, demand for the Spartus line of clocks had increased to the point that non-clock product lines dropped. The clock line was then expanded to include sequential chime and swinging pendulum models with the mechanisms for those designed in-house and the patents assigned to the firm. Electric plastic and wood "decorator" clocks continued to be produced including animated novelty clocks, an electric "anniversary" clock, a backwards running clock, and reproductions of oil paintings with a built-in clock. Many of these continue to be made at this writing. All cases were made and finished in house.

Spartus again became a subsidiary of Kidde in 1973 when that firm obtained LCA. Three years later, certain assets and the use of the name "Waltham" for up-scale decorator clocks were purchased from the Waltham Watch Company. The Waltham line and a line sold under the James C. Huntington name continue to be made and sold through the Spartus sales organization. Included in these lines are tall-case, school regulator, Vienna regulator, and mantle models, some with key-wound 31-day movements and others with quartz movements. All of the Huntington and most of the Waltham models are imported.

Although the "58" synchronous movement remained the mainstay of the firm until it was phased out, a smaller, low-wattage movement was designed in 1980. It was designed and produced for thin-wall non-animated wall clocks and had a limited torque. By the mid-1980s when it became apparent that the popularity of electric clocks was on the decline, Spartus began to phase out this part of its line in favor of quartz clocks. Synchronous movement manufacture was discontinued in 1986, and the movement inventory gradually reduced through its use on a few select models. By early 1992, all synchronous movement assembly had ceased.

Spartus' move into the electronic digital clock business began in 1985 with the establishment of Sigma Electronics, Ltd. in Hong Kong to manufacture LED clocks, timer modules and related products. The manufacturing side of this operation was to move to mainland of China in 1988. Then, in conjunction with the Kienzle firm of Germany, Spartus designed a quartz time and alarm movement and began automated assembly of same in the Louisville plant in 1987. Until that time, they had been importing their battery movements. Hanson PLC, a British-American industrial management firm purchased the Spartus operation in 1987 and it continues under their ownership.

This paper is based on the records and recollections of the author and his present and former colleagues: Martha Daly, Allen Gold, Gordon Ingham, Keith Hudson, and Allan Rubin, all of whom were at one time or another, with the Spartus organization.

C.M. Jauch, # 78169

Applying the principles of telegraphy to horology was an idea which fascinated a number of inventors beginning just after the Civil War, and by the 1880s electromagnetic systems consisting of a master clock and secondary or "slave" dials were gaining both reliability and popularity in a skeptical world. The concept of simply and inexpensively constructed clock movements sharing the accuracy of a fine well-maintained regulator by virtue of being connected to it undoubtedly received its greatest impetus through the inventive genius and labors of Charles D. Warner of Ansonia, Connecticut who established The Standard Electric Time Company in nearby New Haven in 1884.

In its early days, Standard manufactured secondary clocks but offered as masters a line of regulators made by the Self-Winding Clock Company of Brooklyn, New York, to which it added contacts for advancing the secondaries, along with necessary controls and "Warner System" decals. By 1892, Standard had relocated to Waterbury, Connecticut and was purchasing incomplete regulators from Seth Thomas to which it proceeded to add its own once-a-minute electric winding mechanism as well as the aforementioned components. Additionally, convenience of operation often meant inclusion of a "Warner's Patent Electric Gauge" — a device that indicated the flow of electricity to and through the system — and at least one pilot dial within the master clock case.

As the firm continued to progress, it manufactured more and more of the master clock on its own, and introduced several distinctive case styles. A program machine had been developed to ring electric bells or activate other types of signals automatically at times determined by where holes had been punched in a paper disc (later an endless tape or ribbon) which, like the secondary timepieces, was advanced in one-minute increments by the master clock which also dictated, through a separate series of contacts, the duration (usually five seconds) that the signals would sound once engaged. Thus, by providing perfectly synchronized time in every room of even our largest buildings, together with the automatic ringing of bells at any minute desired,

Master clock with self-winding movement. *Left,* front view. *Right,* door opened to show paper tape program mechanism.

Warner's clock and program systems were particularly adapted to the needs of schools and colleges. Factories, railroad stations, hotels, banks, department stores, hospitals, government buildings, and the like all served to augment the market.

In 1893, Warner hired an energetic lad of 19, Gerald L. Riggs, as "jack of all trades." Within four years Riggs was able to purchase The Standard Electric Time Company for six thousand dollars, assuming all its debts. Under the control of Mr. Riggs, the company continued to expand and improve its product line. As early as 1896 electric tower clocks were offered, "operating one to four dials of any diameter." By 1910, branch offices had been established in Chicago, New York, Boston, and San Francisco. Riggs moved the company to Springfield, Massachusetts in 1912, where it grew and prospered as never before, and soon became an acknowledged leader in school clock systems.

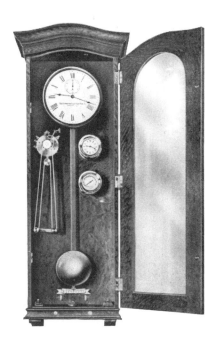

Catalog illustration of 60-beat 2-circuit program model with pilot dial and battery gauge in case.

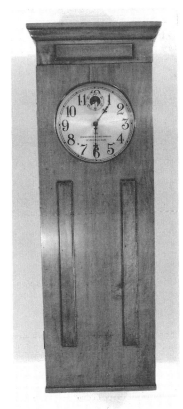

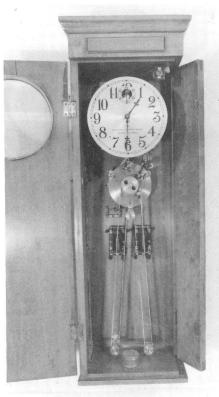

Transition model program master using a synchronous motor. *Left,* front view. *Right,* doors opened to show center mounted program mechanism and no pendulum.

AC synchronous motor had started to replace the pendulum and escapement in master clocks, and by the early fifties, began to appear in secondary

Slave clock. (Photo courtesy of Lehr Dircks)

clocks as well. The last pendulum-type master clock was built in 1957.

In 1968, Standard was acquired by Johnson Controls, Inc., which ten years later sold it to Faraday, Inc. Faraday moved the company from Springfield to Tecumseh, Michigan headquarters in 1981, where it remains in business today as America's oldest maker of electric clocks.

Suggested Reading

1. Swetsky, M., 1989: Standard Electric Time Co. Clock, *NAWCC Bulletin,* 31:354.

2. Coombe, W.M., et al, 1991: New Life for a Tower Clock, *NAWCC Bulletin,* 33:125-129.

3. Anonymous, 1908: Standard Electric Time Company; Master and Slave Clock Descriptions, *The Journal of Electrical Horology,* April.

Jeffrey R. Wood, #2271

The education market also provided Standard with an excellent opportunity to diversify — first, by producing electric fire alarm systems which operated from the same battery used to power the clocks; then, came telephone intercom equipment, normally installed in conjunction with a clock system plug board which permitted individual class room bells and/or buzzers to be assigned to any program circuit (or none at all) and sounded separately for telephone signalling or any other special purpose. Science laboratory timers were introduced which were operated from a seconds ticker attachment connected to the master clock pendulum. School and college laboratories also needed a selection of voltages and currents for experiments and demonstrations. Standard came out with power distribution panels designed specifically to meet this need.

As Standard Electric Time continued into the Depression Era, electric clock systems were developed which no longer relied on batteries, and would automatically reset themselves after a power outage. In the late 1930s, the

STANFORD PRODUCTS

In operation for only about 18 months during 1931 and 1932, the Stanford Products Company's plant was located in Daly City, two blocks from the San Francisco city line. It was owned by a David Spector. Developed in Menlo Park, near Stanford University, these synchronous motor clocks took their name from that school. They were not widely distributed and, as a result, are seldom seen in the Midwest and East.

Monochron bakelite alarm.

About 40 people were employed by the company, which made electric alarm clocks, electric clocks with perpetual calendars and standard electric timepieces. A particular feature of the product was a motor designed so that it could be readily disassembled for cleaning and repair.

Early models were cased in bakelite, but often spray painted to the wholesaler's specifications. A few chime clocks were also produced and cased in walnut. Much of what this company achieved seemed to parallel the activities of the Hammond Clock Company during that same time period. Although half a continent apart — with no evident connection — they both featured calendar models, developed movements which were self-starters, and used a small spring-and-governor arrangement to bridge the power interruptions that were all too frequent in the early thirties.

According to reports, the firm was well into the manufacturing process, had entered the local market and was ready to go into greater production and wider distribution when Hammond announced its Bichronous movement, which also bridged power interruptions. Because of Hammond's wide advertising programs and the fact that their "Duokron" power-bridging model was developed after Hammond's, Stanford was not able to compete on a national scale and production stopped sometime in 1932.

Duokron models. *Upper,* boudoir. *Lower,* kitchen.

Wall model monochron.

Suggested Reading

1. Theobald, George, 1962: The Stanford Products Company of San Francisco, Calif., *NAWCC Bulletin,* X:421-423.

George Theobald, FNAWCC, #3077

STROMBERG ELECTRIC MANUFACTURING COMPANY

Just 23 years old when he immigrated to the United States from his native Sweden, Alfred Stromberg had completed his apprenticeship with Eller & Company, the oldest electrical firm there. Because of his considerable electrical skills, he found work with Bell Telephone in Pennsylvania.

A few years later, he moved to Chicago where he again found employment with another Bell company and met a kindred spirit, Androv Carlson. Being ambitious people, they formed the Stromberg-Carlson Company in 1894 and began to manufacture magneto telephones, switchboards, and central exchanges. By 1902, with Bell Telephone acquiring independent telephone companies and suppliers, Home Telephone of Rochester, New York bought the major interest in the Stromberg-Carlson operation to assure a continued supply of equipment. The plant and the principals were both moved to Rochester. Stromberg and Carlson sold their interest in the business there in 1905 and returned, once again, to Chicago. Here Alfred Stromberg began

Wall master with mercury pendulum.

three new ventures: Stromberg Motor Devices, Stromberg Carburetor, and Stromberg Electric Manufacturing.

Stromberg became interested in the mechanical devices used to stamp incoming mail in many offices. They were crudely designed and required that the date stamp be changed daily, if the clerk remembered! He decided that this could be done much more efficiently by the use of electric impulses and under his guidance an electro-mechanical time stamp machine was developed by C.M. Crook. This remote controlled stamp was patented as the Model 1 Time Stamp and manufacture began at the plant at 23 S. Jefferson Street in Chicago.

The firm grew and by 1908 larger headquarters were acquired, again in Chicago, and the company was incorporated. Under Stromberg's guidance the company patented and manufactured time stamps, job clocks, program units, and secondary wall clocks, all using remote master controls which they also made.

Movement, which can be configured to run a time stamp, from wall master on right.

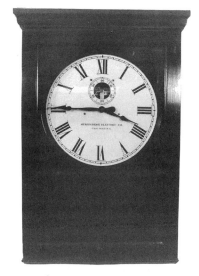

Wall mounted master with vibrator motor.

sales offices in 24 United States cities, a subsidiary in Canada and gross sales of over $1,000,000.

The General Time Corporation purchased all the shares in Stromberg on December 1935. After operating the firm for 30 years, General Time sold it. Since then there have been several owners with the firm owned and operated as a division of the New Haven (CT) Manufacturing Corporation since 1989. Currently, they continue to list a Model 414 Payroll Recorder which is quite like the Model 15 or 14 made in the 1930s. Although there have been some cosmetic changes, it is almost identical in operation and mechanically to the earlier models, clear evidence of the quality engineering and manufacture seen in Stromberg's early products.

Thanks in part to a growing economy, Alfred Stromberg's company grew rapidly. With the growth of other businesses, there was an increasing need for accuracy — accuracy that assured that the time stamp in the mail room agreed with the job clock on the factory floor and the wall clock in the bosses' offices. Stromberg's products met these requirements and they were well regarded. By 1929, when the company incorporated in Delaware, they had

Suggested Reading

1. MacNeal, Harry B., 1934: *The Story of Independent Telephony*, Independent Pioneer Telephone Association.

2. Stromberg Division, 1961: *General Sales and Service Manual*, Thomaston, CT, General Time Corporation.

Joseph Bourell #49251

THE SYNCHRONOME CO. LTD.

The story of the Synchronome Company of Alperton, Middlesex, England centers around the checkered life of Frank Hope-Jones who turned the despised electric clock into a reliable time measurement instrument. The complexities of his career are too great to be discussed here, but his interest in electric horology began when he visited an exhibition with G.B. Bowell, an apprentice working with his brother who designed and built electrically-operated wind organs. Both young men felt that they could improve on the electric clocks on display. The first development was an electrically-reset remontoire driving a dead-beat escapement to impulse the pendulum. The advantage with this arrangement was the positive making and breaking of the electric contacts to permit half-minute pulses of any power required to impulse slave clock systems. It was the first successful electric master clock to be produced commercially in quantity in Britain. Before success was achieved,

however, Bowell and Hope-Jones had an acrimonious dispute which led to the permanent alienation of the two men. Bowell was the creative element, yet he never fulfilled his early promise and died a forgotten man. Hope-Jones was the entrepreneur who founded the Synchronome Company in Clerkenwell when Bowell left his syndicate. The company survives in a different form to this day.

Its fortunes were founded on what Hope-Jones termed his "momentum break," the electric contacts were arranged so that the force of resetting the remontoire was transmitted through the contacts. The remontoire contact then was moved rapidly away by reason of its momentum from the impulsing contact when the latter was suddenly arrested by a fixed stop. This contact system can work reliably over millions of operations, thus the master clock was rendered completely reliable. Hope-Jones attempted to get this idea

adopted as a fundamental principle in electric timekeeping, but it proved to be only one solution to contact problems.

At this time, the firm now known as Gents of Leicester was also drawn into the field of electric horology and had two men, Langman and Ball, designing electric clocks. They produced a master clock in which the pendulum was driven directly by the remontoire, the pendulum turning a count wheel to control the impulsing of the system. Hope-Jones was an avid researcher of patents in the Patent Office in London and took Ball's ideas for his own directly-driven pendulum, to produce the well known master clock design that was used without radical change from 1905 until Synchronome ceased manufacturing clocks in the 1950s. The case might change and various auxiliaries might be added, but the basic design for the base plate and layout became permanent for the ordinary run-of-the-mill master clocks produced by Synchronome. Hope-Jones, realizing that his design was easy to copy, circumvented difficulties by selling base plates and components to anyone who wished to make a Synchronome clock for himself. These amateur-constructed clocks show the greatest deviation from the norm.

The precision clock used by many astronomical observatories at the beginning of the twentieth century was the Reifler, a mechanically-driven regulator with its pendulum in an evacuated container. Reifler (of Germany) purloined Hope-Jones' system to rewind his regulator and Hope-Jones became interested in producing a precision regulator of his own. The first model, designed by W.H. Shortt, using an inertia impulsing system, was a failure and only a few clocks were produced. Their performance varied little from the normal Synchronome clock which would keep time within a second or so per week. These new clocks had Invar pendulum rods rated at the National Physical Laboratory, Teddington, and were individually compensated to correct the final temperature errors.

Shortt was basically a railroad engineer who was given the task of accurately timing various operations. This eventually led him, through sponsorship of Hope-Jones (who put the manufacturing resources of Synchronome at his disposal), to the concept of the Shortt Free Pendulum clock. In this clock the master pendulum swings freely in an evacuated container and is impulsed every half-minute by a small gravity remontoire, released by a slave clock pendulum, which relieved the master pendulum of all duties. The slave clock (a slightly modified standard Synchronome master clock) was given a slight losing rate and periodically corrected, as needed, to run in synchronism with the Free Pendulum. The precise time was given each time the remontoire fell off the impulsing point of the master pendulum. The daily error rate was reduced to a few milliseconds, and thus in 1921, when the first Shortt-Synchronome Free Pendulum was set to work at the Edinburgh Observatory, it set a new standard of timekeeping for the whole world. Ninety-nine of these free pendulum clocks were made by one man — Bill Jones (not related to Frank Hope-Jones). Observatories world-wide adopted them. For the first time it was possible to show the effect of the nutation of the earth and the influence of

 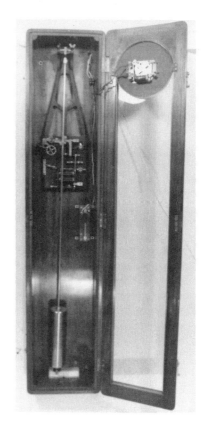

Master clock. *Left,* front view. *Right,* door open to show works.

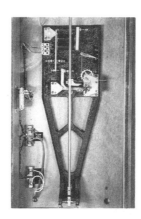

Close-up of Synchronome movement.

diurnal gravitational effects caused by the moon. In other words, the measurement of time by the pendulum clock had virtually reached the practical limit of its development. This great triumph, which had been sought for centuries by clockmakers, was not to last long because of the development of quartz crystal oscillators for use in time measurement devices. The accuracy of quartz crystal oscillators soon led to the abandonment of all other types of clocks in observatories. The quartz crystal clock was so accurate that it demonstrated that the earth itself is not a perfect timekeeper — long suspected, but not possible to prove before.

Thousands of Synchronome electric master and slave clocks were produced over a period of fifty years. These clocks are of such high quality that they exhibit little wear and will probably last for centuries if treated correctly. The count wheel is the most vulnerable part to wear, the gathering click and its jewel, the most fragile component; but these parts can be easily made again. There are no spare components available from the Synchronome-Tann company of today. It is believed that any inventory is held in store for those clock systems still in use and serviced by the firm. Moreover, the firm will not respond to inquires about Synchronome clocks. The whole range of Synchronome electric clocks form collectors' items today.

Suggested Reading

1. Hope-Jones, Frank, 1949: *Electrical Timekeeping,* 2nd ed., London, England, N.A.G. Press.

2. Hope-Jones, Frank, 1931: *Electrical Clocks,* London, England, N.A.G. Press.

3. Aked, Charles K., 1977: *Electrifying Time,* Ticehurst, Sussex, England, The Antiquarian Horological Society.

Charles K. Aked, FNAWCC, #29401

TIFFANY ELECTRIC MANUFACTURING COMPANY

Standard dome model with dome removed. *Left*, front view. *Right*, back view.

Two-contact dome model with dome removed. *Left*, front view. *Right*, view of movement.

The Tiffany Never-Wind clock was first patented in 1901 by George Steele Tiffany, a New Jersey resident. The clocks were originally made in New York City. Later, the firm moved to Buffalo, possibly about 1904, and finally to Dunkirk, New York. The earliest models came in wooden cases with glass sides and were somewhat taller than those produced later. There were also some models under a glass dome. All had a torsion pendulum and were electrically impulsed by means of a contact, completed at the end of each revolution of the pendulum, thus their designation as the Double Contact Type.

Additional patents were awarded in 1904 and covered a simpler and less expensive Single Contact model which was impulsed at the end of rotation in only one direction. These clocks were most often manufactured in four-glass crystal regulator cases and in brass-based dome models, apparently in re-

National Magnetic model. *Upper*, front view. *Lower*, back removed to show the movement.

sponse to the public preference. An extensive advertising campaign was launched shortly after these models were introduced, and large quantities of these clocks were made and sold during the first quarter of the 20th century, finally succumbing to the inexpensive synchronous motor plug-in clocks that dominated the market from the late 1920s onward.

The pendulum used on the earlier models consisted of a pair of brass balls with the suspension ribbon connected to their junction. The adjustment to set the rate was accomplished by a knurled regulator which moved the balls closer together or farther apart, similar to the governors used in machinery of that era. The later models employed a pair of inverted brass cups as the pendulum, adjusted by a sliding device which effectively lengthened or shortened the suspension ribbon by

Niagara wall model.

means of a pinching action; not altogether unlike the curb pins acting on the hairspring of the hairspring of a watch or clock.

These clocks were also made under license by other makers and may be found with the names Cloister, National Magnetic and Niagara, in addition to the more usual Tiffany Never-Wind. Despite the lack of temperature-compensation material in the suspension, the clocks kept reasonably good time and enjoyed exceptional sales during the company's existence. It was one of the most popular American-made electric clocks.

Suggested Reading

1. Amend, Arthur, 1982: The Tiffany "Never-Wind" Clock — Description; Repairs and Adjustment, *NAWCC Bulletin*, XXIV: 494.

2. Shenton, Alan & Shenton, Rita, 1985: *The Price Guide to Collectable Clocks*, London, England, Antiques Collectors Club.

3. Hagans, Orville R. (ed), 1979: *The Best of J.E. Coleman: Clockmaker*, Denver, CO, American Watchmaker's Institute Press, p. 391.

4. de Magnin, Paul Ron, 1963: Collecting Battery-Powered Clocks, *NAWCC Bulletin*, X:7080

Martin Swetsky, FNAWWC, #31665

Tiffany crystal regulator model.

World War II and Hitler's invasion of Norway caused numerous Norwegians to flee their country and come to the United States. One was Joakim Lehmkuhl, who emigrated in 1941 after having disposed of his family's interest in a shipping firm. In 1944, Lehmkuhl and his United States Time Corporation purchased the Ingersoll-Waterbury Watch Company which, it has been reported, consisted mainly of antiquated machinery in relatively poor condition. At the time of purchase, the firm was engaged in the manufacture of fuses for the military, but had done some research on the manufacture of a plastic alarm clock — in light of restrictions on the non-military use of metal.

Almost immediately, a new factory was built in Middlebury, Connecticut, but it was not until 1945 that the firm was to begin watch production. The Ingersoll name continued to appear on their watches until 1951 when the Timex brand name was introduced on a newly designed wrist watch. Subsequent improvements in that design led to the Model 24 which is still being manufactured. Over 500 million of the basic model 24 movements have been made, according to the firm. In addition to the traditional non-jeweled Model 24, both 11-jewel and 21-jewel versions were made. They were designed by the noted Dutch horologist, George Garbe, who had come to this country to work for Timex and it is reported that 3,000,000 were made during the 1961-1970 run of the jeweled models.

Noting the public's interest in, and the increasing sale of, electric watches with the advent of small efficient dry cells during the war, the Timex firm purchased the Laco Watch of France in 1961 to secure access to their electric movements. The electric watches produced by Timex were quite similar in principle to the Hamilton electrics with a hollow electromagnetic coil mounted on the balance working against a permanent magnet mounted below. It was stated there was little sparking when the contact for the electromagnetic coils circuit was made or broken and that the movement had a contact protecting jewel which served as a "wipe" for the contacts. Over 200,000,000 electrics, in at least six different movement models, were produced before this line was dropped in 1982. Many were designed and made in the company's plants in Pforzheim (Germany), Besancon (France), Dundee (Scotland), and Chemglece (Taiwan) in addition to their Little Rock (Arkansas) plant. All were cased in the United States.

Two balance wheel electric watches. *Left*, ladies. *Right*, Dynabeat men's.

In 1972, Timex marketed its first quartz watch, an analog model, which was a modification of the Model 40 electric. It was designed and originally made in their Middlebury facility, but manufacture was later moved to Little Rock and then to Taiwan. In this model 62, the balance wheel amplitude is controlled by an integrated circuit chip and a quartz crystal, and it has a sweep second hand that does not "jump" as on most quartz watches. Rather, the hand advances six times per second, thus approximately the appearance of other electric- or spring-driven watches. Digital quartz watches were introduced into the line in 1975 with the Timex Model 75 LCD.

During its growth period, Timex built or acquired many manufacturing

Electronic "time zone" model. *Left*, back removed to show works. *Right*, dial view.

facilities outside the United States which have a most definite role in the firm's operations. The Middlebury location continues to be the headquarters and most of the graphic appearance designs are created there. The Bescanon plant, however, is a major manufacturing facility with most of the movement components required for assembly by plants worldwide being produced there. Most screw machine parts, molded plastic parts, and even some flat parts are made in Bescanon and manufacturing designs and case engineering originate in this plant. Moreover, a plant in Feldham (England) produces hands, dials and plastic cases and many watches are assembled in the Philippines, the Virgin Islands and other locations in addition to the United States.

Timex continues as the only domestic company producing a full line of watches, some 500 styles in all, with many produced or assembled in their American plants. Currently, they continue to manufacture several million mechanical watches a year, in addition to their quartz line.

Suggested Reading

1. Price, Howard G., 1985: Timex 21, *NAWCC Bulletin*, XXVII: 421-423.

2. Bailey, Chris H., 1975: *Two Hundred Years of American Clocks and Watches*, Englewood Cliffs, NJ, Prentice-Hall, Inc.

3. Miscellaneous documents from the Timex Company.

4. Hagans, Orville R. (ed), 1975: *The Best of J.E. Coleman: Clockmaker*, Denver, CO, American Watchmakers Institute Press.

William F. Keller, #12745

TRINITY CLOCK COMPANY

Records on this firm are relatively scarce, but it seems to have been a part of the Trinity Toy and Novelty Company. It appears to have begun clock production about 1908 or 1909, based on a date found in a clock in the author's collection, and to have continued manufacture until the mid-1920s.

In so far as can be determined, the movements remained unchanged during the entire time and they often appeared under the name American Self-Winding Clock Company. There is no evidence of any advertising having been done and the clocks were basically "premium" clocks given to news boys who sold enough subscriptions.

Case styles were varied and there was generally no protection for the hands, although we have seen a few models with glasses. Designed to run on two #6 dry cells (three volts) the clocks would run for about a year on a set of cells.

None of the clocks seen have serial numbers, so it is impossible to estimate just how many were produced. These clocks seem to be quite scarce, however, and we know not why. Particularly scarce are those bearing the American Self-Winding name.

Elmer G. Crum, FNAWCC, #33463

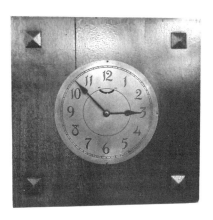

Round top mantle model. *Upper*, front view. *Lower*, back removed to show movement.

Sharp gothic model. *Upper*, front view. *Lower*, close-up of double weighted drive mechanism.

Square office wall model. (Photo courtesy of Lehr Dircks)

Square mission style wall model.

WALLACE AND TIERNAN PRODUCTS, INC.

Wallace and Tiernan Products, Inc. of Belleville, New Jersey was well established in the field of precision instruments for the scientific and aircraft industries. During World War II they made timing units for the U.S. Army and Navy and aircraft instruments for virtually every airplane that was built for the war effort. The quality of these products was unmatched anywhere.

Just why and when they began making clocks is not clear, but based on the five-or-so case styles seen by the author, a good guess is that they began somewhere between 1920 and 1930. All of the movements were housed in cases of good construction.

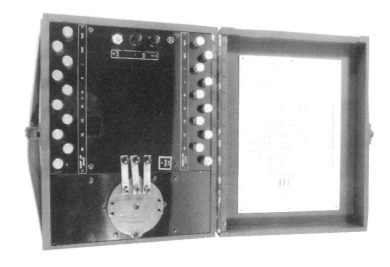

Artillery timer. *Above,* timer in it's case. *Left,* timer mechanism removed to show works.

Mini schoolhouse. *Upper,* front view. *Right,* back removed to show movement.

Rather simple in construction, the clocks allow for little or no adjustment and are insulated from the case itself by rubber grommets. We presume the grommets were added to reduce the loud ticking sounds caused by the pinwheel escapement.

The clock was designed to operate on 3 volts using two D cells in series. All clocks examined to date have had a built in battery container.

Little or nothing has appeared in the literature regarding this firm and information about it would be appreciated.

Suggested Readings

1. de Magnin, Paul Ron, 1963: Collecting Battery-Powered Clocks, *NAWCC Bulletin,* X:707-708

Elmer G. Crum, FNAWCC, #33463

The movement of the Wallace clock was rather unique in design, not so much for its electric or weight-lifting principles, but for the use of a pinwheel escapement in an electric clock. The plates were stamped and the movement shows very little of the quality that Wallace was capable of producing.

Banjo model.

WALTHAM ELECTRIC CLOCK COMPANY

The story of the Waltham Electric Clock Company is interesting, not only for its clocks, but because of some of the individuals involved. Chartered in New Hampshire in 1890, the company began operations in an upper story of the Stark Machine Shop. At that time the reported principals were John Stark of the Stark Tool Company and Walter K. Menns, a British subject. The company's primary interest was in the production of movements for electrically operated slave clocks and other timing equipment that could take signals from their master clocks. The combined talents of Stark, whose firm manufactured watchmaker's lathes, and Menn who held several patents for electric clocks would seem to have been an ideal partnership.

The firm, as originally organized, had no association with the Waltham Watch Company even though it changed its name to the Waltham Clock Company after about two years of operation. In 1898, the company was evidently reorganized and the partnership then included Stark, William C. Henry and Thomas W. Sheppard. This arrangement lasted for 15 years when Henry's death, coupled with financial problems,

Catalog illustration of late model (circa 1940).

caused them to sell the assets to the Waltham Watch Company.

By the spring of 1914, the clock-making equipment had been installed in the watch factory and established as the Waltham Clock Department of the Waltham Watch Company with Thomas Sheppard as Superintendent. Clocks continued to be manufactured over the next 10 years, with Waltham making the movements and cases being purchased from the Herschede Hall Clock Company. It appears that a disastrous strike in 1924 seriously affected the clock operation and that the production

of pendulum clocks was more or less discontinued. Electric clocks and speedometers were made into the 1940s.

In 1948, the O.B. McClintock Company purchased the Electric Clock Division of the Waltham Clock Company including rights to their patent #2,292,625 for a small synchronous clock motor. McClintock manufactured alarm and time only clocks under this patent for a short time. Waltham later sold the right to use its name on up-scale decorator clocks to the Spartus firm which continues to produce clocks bearing the Waltham name.

Suggested Reading

1. Burt, Edwin B., 1958: Derry Manufacturing Company, *NAWCC Bulletin*, VIII:148.

2. Bundens, Jr. W.D., 1976: Your NAWCC Museum — The Waltham Electric Clock Co., *NAWCC Bulletin*, XVIII:217.

3. Bailey, O.H., 1975. *Two Hundred Years of American Clocks and Watches*, Englewood Cliffs, NJ, Prentice-Hall, Inc.

William F. Keller, #12745

WARREN TELECHRON COMPANY

As mentioned earlier in this volume, Henry Warren must be considered the father of what most people know as electric timekeeping. He called it "synchronous timekeeping." Those who purchased his clocks came to know them as Telechrons — clocks that plugged into an electric power line and never needed winding. In their heyday, before quartz clocks took over, Telechron clocks and their clones were found in virtually every home and place of business. They were dependable, except for an occasional power outage, and many ran for 30 years or more without repair. They never needed new batteries.

How did Warren's system work? A small synchronous motor will run at a speed exactly corresponding to the frequency of the alternating current of the power supply to which it is connected. The motor needs only some gears, hands, and a face to be a reliable timekeeper. The key is to main-

Warren battery powered "mystery" clock.

tain the frequency of the line at a constant value, say 60 cycles per second. At the time Warren first developed his synchronous motors and clocks, he found that they were off by as much as 10-15 minutes a day — a rather disappointing situation! Therefore, he set out to rectify things.

What he did was revolutionary and, at the time, not too well received by power-generating companies. His solution was to have a synchronous motor clock on the power line along with a separate spring-driven high quality master clock, both at the power station and in view of the plant operator who compared their times. If the two clocks always agreed, power was being maintained at a correct and constant frequency. If the synchronous clock fell behind, the speed of the generators was increased to bring the two clocks into agreement. Similarly, if the synchronous clock began to gain, the generators were slowed to bring the two clocks into agreement. All clocks on the same power supply followed along, keeping correct time.

Henry Warren placed his first master clock (Type A, floor standing with a one-second pendulum) in the"L Street" station of Boston Electric on October 23, 1916. The master was kept correct by comparison twice-a-day with the time signals from the Naval Observatory wireless station NAA near Washington, DC. Thus, timekeeping accuracy, for those who purchased synchronous motor clocks (also made by Warren), advanced rapidly to an error of less than 1/500 of 1%, i.e., the accuracy of the master clock, which was within one second per day.

Persuading other power companies to purchase his master clocks proceeded slowly. Many firms worried about the possible legal consequences of advertising correct time and others simply said, "Who needs it?" Nevertheless, by 1925, some 400 "Type A" clocks had been sold along with many of his "Type B" master clocks (a wall model, slightly

Early Warren Telekron mantle clock. (Photo courtesy of The Hall of History, Schenectady, NY)

Telechron General Electric refrigerator model.

Warren "B" master clock.

Warren "A" master clock, to left. *Upper*, front view. *Lower*, close-up of dial.

less accurate). Moreover, the use of the master clocks, ensuring a more constant frequency, enabled more and more power companies to interconnect and share their generated power.

Telechron office wall model.

Telechron miniature banjo.

Telechron nickel plated alarm with lighted dial.

Hotpoint range timer made by Telechron.

Telechron system timer.

Telechron Selector model with timed switch circuit.

Telechron digital model.

Although he is best remembered for his developments in the synchronous time area, Warren actually began his horologic work almost ten years earlier. His first patent for an electric clock was issued in 1909 and he formed the Warren Clock Company in 1912 to make battery clocks, which were not too successful. After 1916 he moved to AC clocks, calling them Telechron (at first Telekron) in 1919. By 1926 it was the Warren Telechron Company; Telechron, Inc. in 1943; and by 1948 the Clock and Timer Department of the General Electric Company. GE bought a half interest in 1917 and full interest in 1943. In 1979 Timex bought the operation from GE but resold it to local management in 1983. Today, the Telechron Company, somewhat downsized, thrives in Ashland, Massachusetts making clocks and timing motors.

Suggested Reading

1. Anderson, J.M., 1991: Henry Warren and His Master Clocks, *NAWCC Bulletin*, 33:374-395.

2. Cramer, H.R. 1978: Warren Battery Clock, *The Journal of Electrical Horology*, November.

Telechron plastic alarm.

Typical 1930s bakelite cathedral case housing a Telechron movement.

John M. Anderson #7171

Principals of the Benedict and Burnham Manufacturing Company of Waterbury, Connecticut were largely responsible for the organization of the Waterbury Clock Company. As producers of brass, several of the clock firms in the area were their customers. Also, they were investors in Jerome Manufacturing Company and were well acquainted with the clock business.

That they should eventually desire to have their own clockmaking factory could be considered a natural development and by 1855 plans for such an operation were underway. The Waterbury Clock Company was formed as a joint stock firm on March 5, 1857 with most of the stockholders being associated with Benedict and Burnham. In its early years the firm employed a number of veteran clock and case makers including Chauncey and Noble Jerome and Silas Terry. Although these men had no financial interest in the firm, their efforts did much to help establish Waterbury's name and reputation in the industry.

By 1870, the firm had expanded several times and employed 142 workers. During the 12 months prior to June of that year, over 82,000 clocks had been manufactured. Three years later, they were manufacturing seven different one-day movements and six different eight-day movements. Production demanded that a new and larger movement factory be added to their growing factory complex.

Fast becoming a major clock producer, Waterbury entered the non-jewelled

Bracket alarm.

Bakelite alarm.

watch business in 1878 with a watch designed by Daniel Buck, to be followed three years later by the "Jumbo" designed by Archibald Bannatyne. This watch greatly interested the principals in R.H. Ingersoll & Brother, a Chicago mail-order business which purchased 1,000 "Jumbos," beginning what was to be a very profitable relationship for over 20 years.

Hard-hit by the decline in sales caused by the Great Depression after the very prosperous period of the 1920s and with aged and often obsolete equipment, the company was placed in receivership in 1932. A reorganization resulted and a new firm, Ingersoll-Waterbury was formed with a capitalization of half-a-million dollars. It was during this period that they introduced the familiar Disney character watches including the very popular Mickey Mouse model and began the manufacture of electric clocks.

World War II saw a switch to military production. The firm listed timing fuses, oil gauges, torpedo gyroscopes, and screw jacks among the many products manufactured for the military. Early in 1942, the firm was sold to Norwegian interests and a new modern factory was built in Middlebury, Connecticut. In 1944, the company's name was changed to the United States Time Corporation, ending the nearly 90-year history of a firm bearing the Waterbury name.

Suggested Reading

1. Milham, Willis T., 1948: The World's Columbian Exposition Watch, *Bulletin of the National Association of Watch and Clock Collectors*, III:423-425.

2. Ly, Tran Duy, 1989: *American Clocks*, Arlington, VA, Arlington Book Company.

3. Ly, Tran Duy, 1989: *Waterbury Clocks*, Arlington, VA, Arlington Book Company.

William F. Keller, #12745

Westclox

The Western Clock Company owes its genesis to The United States Clock Company which was organized in Peru, Illinois in December, 1885 to manufacture clocks using a rather revolutionary method of casting gear bodies and other parts. Although the Terrys had used cast lantern pinion end pieces almost fifty years earlier, it remained for Charles Stahlberg of Waterbury, Connecticut to improve on their techniques and secure a patent (#326,602) for the process. Stahlberg and several others from Waterbury, who may have

had experience in clockmaking, were instrumental in forming the new firm.

The exact reason for their choosing Peru is unknown, but it was attractive for its natural resources including coal, zinc and lead, and for its rail and water transportation. Another possible attraction to Stahlberg, a German, was the area's large population of German immigrants, who had come there after the Civil War. The United Clock Company's early clocks were unreliable, and the firm's funds ran out before

necessary improvements could be made, forcing them into bankruptcy in 1887.

The firm was reorganized as the Western Clock Company later that year, which also failed, and then as the Western Clock Manufacturing Company in July of 1888. The largest shareholder in the later firm was F.W. Matthiessen of the Matthiessen and Heggler Zinc Company, LaSalle, Illinois. One of his reasons for becoming involved was his belief that the company would help stimulate the area's

Ben Franklin model using a Sangamo motor (circa 1934).

Sterling auto clock made for the after market.

economy. This time things went well and the company prospered. Numerous product improvements were made and patented and their market increased rapidly. By 1907, they were said to be producing 6,000 clocks a day. Clocks made up through 1903 can be identified by the date of Stahlberg's patent, September 22, 1888, on the back. Many of the early movements were time only, bore no company name, and are often found in cast cases from novelty clock firms.

In 1908, Western began the manufacture of its famous Big Ben model. The name was a registered trade mark and is used on certain of their clocks to this day, although the works and cases have been changed many times. The official company name was shortened to Western Clock Company in 1912 about the time the smaller Baby Ben model was first made.

Western's purchase, in 1928, of the Sterling Clock Company of Meridan, Connecticut, makers of electrically-wound automobile clocks, appears to have been an effort to capitalize on the use of clocks by the growing automotive industry. They closed Sterling's Connecticut plant and moved the entire operation to their LaSalle, Illinois facility. At that time, Sterling was said

Wood-cased Big Ben alarm with Sangamo self-starting motor (circa 1931).

Greenwich self-starting alarm using a Sangamo motor (circa 1937).

Early Sterling auto clock made to auto maker's specifications.

Country Club manual-start model with buzzer alarm (circa 1938).

to have a market for 30,000 clocks per year, designed and made on order for specific automobile makers.

The General Time Instruments Corporation, formed in 1930 as a holding company for Western Clock and Seth Thomas, approached the Sangamo Electric Company in December of that year about the possibility of buying Sangamo's synchronous motors for use in their clocks. Sangamo advised that the motors were available only to the Hamilton-Sangamo Clock Company, a joint venture between Sangamo and the Hamilton Watch Company. The upshot was that General Time bought Hamilton-Sangamo, including all rights to the use of the motors in April, 1931.

Four months after the Hamilton-Sangamo purchase, Western Clock Company's first synchronous electric clocks were placed on the market. They were self-starting models with motors purchased from Sangamo Electric, and the Big Ben models the first available followed by several others.

By 1932, Western Clock had developed its own manual-start synchronous motors, with only the coil of the motor being made outside the LaSalle, Illinois plant. Manual-start clocks were introduced because they could be made and sold at a much lower price. For example, the Silent Knight self-start electric retailed at $4.95 in 1936, whereas the Country Club manual-start retailed at $2.50.

The name of the company was officially changed to Westclox in 1936, a name that had been a trade-mark since 1909. Two years later, a Westclox designed self-starting synchronous motor (patent # 2,015,042) was marketed. It had a large rotor contained between plates with the field coil located away from the rotor to keep the bearings cool. A smaller motor of similar design was introduced in 1940 and used in such clocks as the Baby Ben.

The next self-starting motor, introduced in 1948, had an exposed rotor and integral coil and in the late 1950s, a sealed rotor motor which was detachable from the field coil was introduced.

In March of 1962, Ralph Preiser was named the Chief Engineer of Industrial and New Products and during his

Big Ben chime alarm (circa 1939).

Moonbeam alarm (circa 1941).

Switch clock appliance timer (circa 1949).

tenure a unique clock movement was developed. Jim Whitaker of Granville, Illinois who knew Preiser and talked with him at length about the movement states: "I call it an ambient electric clock movement since...(it) runs off of electricity that is in the air around us, when we are in a building or place that is wired for electricity and the power is on. The clock movement is not plugged in anywhere.... The movement had an auxiliary flashlight battery that ran it whenever it was removed from electrical surroundings. There were four of these movements made and cased at a cost of twenty-five thousand dollars ($25,000.00) apiece for a total of $100,000.00. Mr. Preiser had one of the clocks in his personal collection which the writer was privileged to examine.... (He) told me that development of the clock movement ceased, in favor of quartz movements."

According to Jesse Coleman, all departments of Westclox became involved in

Digital alarm (circa 1970).

the development of a quartz crystal clock late in 1968. He states that it used "three separate modules — a quartz electronic module, a synchronous induction micromotor module, and a precision time-train module." Westclox and Seth Thomas, its sister company, both cataloged clocks using this mechanism and they were said to be the first "reasonably" priced commercial clocks in the market. Seth Thomas models, some nine in number, sold for from $65.00 to $175.00 and the ten Westclox models carried a catalog price of from $50.00 to $500.00, not so reasonably priced compared to the price of quartz timepieces today.

General Tire Instruments, the owner of Westclox, became a division of Talley Industries of Seattle, Washington in May of 1970 following a shareholders' fight. Both spring- and electrically-powered clocks bearing the Westclox name continue to be produced today, many of them manufactured outside the United States.

Suggested Reading.

1. Miller, A.H., & Miller, D.M., 1977: *Illinois Horology*, Published for the 1977 NAWCC National Convention, Chicago.

2. Tjarks, R.C., & Stoddard, W.S., 1983: Introduction to Westclox, *NAWCC Bulletin*, XXV:447-463.

3. Hagans, O.R. (ed), 1979: *The Best of J.E. Coleman: Clockmaker*, Denver, CO, American Watchmakers Institute Press, pp. 69, 88-89.

Richard C. Tjarks, #18,725
William S. Stoddard, #57,911

SIR CHARLES WHEATSTONE

Charles Wheatstone, a most remarkable man with an extremely complex personality, was born in Gloucester (England) in February 1802. He was the son of a music-seller, William Wheatstone. In 1806, the family moved to London and it was while at school there that he exhibited a trait that was to dog him the rest of his life. He won the Gold Medal for proficiency in French and this award required that the prize winner recite a speech after the award was given. He absolutely refused to speak despite all sorts of threats and coaxing, so he forfeited the coveted prize.

When he was 14 years old, he was placed with his uncle Charles at 436 Strand, London to learn the trade of musical instruments, but his father took him away after a few months so he could study on his own with books borrowed from the Society of Arts which was nearby. A proper, although biased, report on the life of Sir Charles and his numerous accomplishments in acoustics, music and electricity, his uncanny ability to decode secret messages and his total mastery of French is given in Brian Bowers' book listed below. All this is beyond the scope of this paper, which considers his involve-

ment in timekeeping and time measurement.

The title of "Professor" was an honorary one bestowed upon him by King's College, London University. He gave very few lectures because of his paranoic fear of audiences. In later years, this led to his fleeing from the lecture hall in the Royal Institute and his lecture being read by Michael Faraday. It was at the Royal Institute, shortly before his death in Paris on October 19, 1875, that his final abortive attempt at electric timekeeping was set. An electric clock system installed in

1873 and removed shortly after Wheatstone's death, is the final confirmation of the schizophrenic and plagiaristic character of Wheatstone, but more on this later.

It was not until his 1840 meeting with Alexander Bain that Wheatstone had any thoughts on electric timekeeping or the automatic printing of messages by the electric telegraph. As a result of that meeting, Wheatstone deceived Bain and stole the details of his electric clock, had it constructed by his workman John Lamb, and passed it off as his own design at the Royal Society, London, in 1840. The written material on the clock, supplied by Wheatstone, has mysteriously vanished from the Society Archives. He did not speak to the assembled audience personally and the event was only reported and not included in the Society's journal, as was the usual practice.

Wheatstone was supreme in the measurement of short durations of time and it was from this work that he developed his "Chronescope" which applied his knowledge of acoustics and electricity to the electromagnetic control of a weight-driven clock. The time-measuring element of the instrument depended on the periodicity of a vibrating reed maintained by a flow of air; or, in earlier models, by a weight. The only electric part was the electromagnet used to start and stop the timing period.

Evidently, the resounding 1845 legal defeat of Wheatstone by Alexander Bain in connection with electric clock systems dissuaded him from further attempts at electric timekeeping. He did, however, purloin the design of a "new" electric clock system devised by his mechanic, Augustus Stroh, and passed it off as his own. Manufactured by the Electric Telegraph Company, it is well described in Frank Hope-Jones *Electrical Timekeeping*, but the author misleads one into thinking that this clock was the worst ever designed from the viewpoint of accurate timekeeping. The fact is that it was never intended to be a timekeeper per se, but merely a generator converting mechanical energy, provided by a large weight, into an alternating current with a periodicity of one Hertz. This alternating current was used to drive synchronous slave clocks — not an original idea. Bain

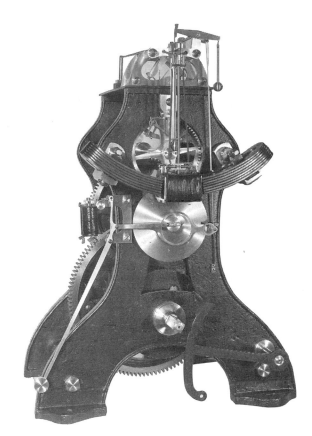

Master clock movement (circa 1870). (Photo courtesy of The Science Museum, London, England)

had used it earlier between Edinburgh and Glasgow to drive a slave pendulum clock.

This so-called "worst clock in the history of electric timekeeping" was not so. It was an ingenious system which had great promise fully realized in the later Magneta System; again, a mechanical system converting mechanical energy from falling weights into electrical energy. This delivered pulses of current, not alternating current. Stroh's synchronization system applied to the generator pendulum ensured absolute accuracy of timekeeping, dependent only on the accuracy of the regulator clock, probably to within a few seconds per week, at most.

The system was, and is, publicized as Wheatstone's electric clock system in spite of Stroh's having taken out the patent (#3028) for its design on October 18, 1869. About six of the systems were constructed, but none of them proved satisfactory in practice. The Royal Institute system was acquired by the Science Museum, London, and continues to have a label showing Wheatstone as the inventor although

there is no evidence to be found in the archives that the work was, indeed, done by Wheatstone.

Although Wheatstone has been said to have made a contribution to the history and development of electric timekeeping, one must say it was minimal, if any. Most of what he is credited for can be said to have been plagiarized. The duality of his personality is clearly evident and is epitomized by the Bain/Wheatstone and Stroh/Wheatstone affairs.

Suggested Reading.

1. Aked, Charles K., 1977: *Electrifying Time*, Ticehurst, Sussex, England, The Antiquarian Horological Society.

2. Aked, Charles K., 1977: *A Conceptus of Electrical Timekeeping*, Ticehurst, Sussex, England, The Antiquarian Horological Society.

3. Bowers, Brian, 1975: *Sir Charles Wheatstone*, London, England.

4. Hope-Jones, Frank, 1949: *Electrical Timekeeping*, 2nd ed. London, England.

Charles K. Aked, FNAWCC, #29401

The Zenith clock is the only known clock to use the principle of expansion and contraction of metals to impulse a pendulum. Known to those who own them as the "hot-wire clocks," they were based on a Deutsches Reich Reichspatentamt (DRP #9650 (a German patent) issued to C.O.J. Jamin in the 1920s.

Though seldom seen in the United States, they were evidently quite popular on the continent since they were designed to operate on any electrical main regardless of its frequency. The clocks contained a small transformer to convert the line voltage to 25v. Operated through the actions of two bimetallic springs activated by the electric current, according to Cammarata, "The time train and pendulum were impulsed on alternate peaks of the pendulum swing in earlier production models."

Later models have only one taint tungsten wire which was alternately heated and allowed to cool, impulsing the pendulum through a simple ratchet and pawl arrangement on a very simple movement. Both models operate on the same basic principle and used a novel micro adjuster that slides on the pendulum rod.

The Zenith concern manufactured numerous other types of electrically operated clocks including master clock systems, tower clocks, and time distribution systems. They should not be confused with the Zenith Radio Corporation of Chicago, however.

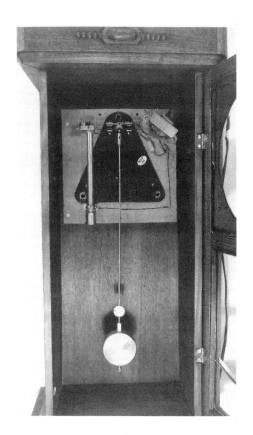

"Hot wire" wall clock. *Left,* front view. *Right,* door opened to show works. Wire is in tube on the left.

Zenith Radio did produce a secondary time standard about 1959 and manufactured a line of clock radios. An outstanding example of the latter is the "Golden Triangle" made from 1961 to 1963. The clock portion was a German-built high-grade balance wheel movement and the radio portion was a modified version of the famous Zenith 500 transistor radio. They were cased in a triangular shaped gold plated and painted case and only 3000 were produced.

Suggested Reading

1. Cammarata, John, 1981: Zenith Hot Wire Electric Clocks, *NAWCC Bulletin,* XXII:185.

Elmer G. Crum, FNAWCC, #33463

Part Three
Identifier Section

THE IDENTIFIER

As stated earlier in this work, there are many firms that were and are involved in the manufacture of electric timepieces. A sizeable percentage of them is represented by specimens in the exhibit on which this book is based, but quite a few are not discussed in the preceding text. In an effort to provide as complete coverage as possible, however, we have added this section which includes those clocks in the exhibit, and a few others, for which no writeup is included and for which we should like to locate information.

Most of these clocks are from companies that have never been researched or covered in any of the literature to which we have had access. Little seems to be known about them. Although we began to assemble data and request papers from our contributors many months ago, and have had superb cooperation and help, there is still much to be done if we are ever to have a relatively complete and authoritative volume on the history of electric timekeeping.

Should seeing the clocks in the exhibit and having the photos and the short legends included here serve to stimulate you to look into such companies as

the Magnetic Clock Company of Hartford, Connecticut which made electrically-wound automobile clocks; the Ever Ready Clock Company of New York which made synchronous powered Plato clocks; or the Mastercrafters Company of Chicago which made many novelty clocks such as the swinging doll, we will feel vindicated in our decision to add this section. Should it help you to identify something you have stuck away in a corner, we will be pleased. Should it induce you to assist in the effort to produce a more definitive and authoritative volume on this often overlooked area of horology, we will be elated and would welcome your help.

Early Kit-Kat clock made by Allied Manufacturing, Seattle, WA.

Synchronous alarm made by Allied Products, Chicago, IL.

Typical 1930s cathedral alarm made by Atlas (USA).

Bardone (France) electric with horseshoe magnet pendulum and coil in bottom of case.

Blue Coal stoker time switch for furnace stoker. Maker unknown.

Brillie (France) mantle model (circa 1914).

Synchronous motor powered Calculograph (East Hanover, N.J) pool room or job timer.

John Browning (London, England) battery clock. *Left,* front view. *Right,* rear view of movement. (Photo courtesy of Tran Duy Ly)

Concord (Switzerland) digital desk clock with battery powered Kundo (Germany) movement.

Diamond Electric Company (Chicago, IL) manual-start synchronous alarm in a bakelite case.

Cincinnati Time Recording (Cincinnati, OH) master clock.

Deho (Germany) self-winding weight-driven wall clock. *Left,* front view. *Right,* dial removed to show large inertia (fly) wheel which helps restore the small weight seen to the left of the pendulum rod.

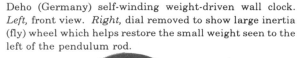

Lincoln brown bakelite cathedral case, time only.

Lincoln synchronous electric tambour made by the Electric Clock Corp. of America (Chicago, IL)

Lincoln brown bakelite cathedral case alarm.

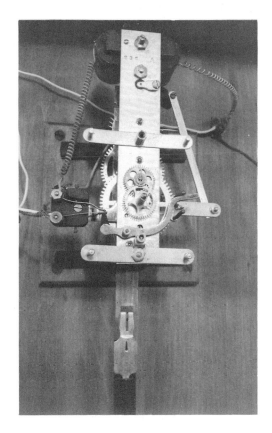

Ever Ready wall clock made by The American Novelty and Manufacturing Co., New York, NY.

Early master clock believed to be from The Silent Electric Clock Co., Ltd. (England). *Left*, front view with face removed. *Right*, close-up of movement.

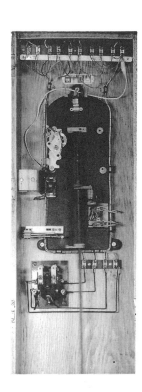

English **Magneta** electrically impulsed clock made by Gillett and Johnston and not to be confused with the Swiss **Magneta**. *Left*, front view. *Right*, close-up of movement.

Gillett & Johnston (England) electrical impulse transmitter used to send time signal by the British Postal Service.

Copernicus Planetarium made by Hughes (USA) and powered by a synchronous motor. Two different screens are shown.

Kalex (New York) synchronous motor version of a world clock (circa 1950).

Gisholt Manufacturing Company (Madison, Wisconsin) is no longer making complicated time mechanisms like this although they are still in business. Their clocks used either Howard #70 or Seth Thomas "F" movements with correction additions to accept Western Union time signals.

Auto clock made by the Magnetic Clock Co. of Hartford, CT.

Synchronous clock made by International Tool & Die Co., Minneapolis, MN.

Kippe (Germany) 220 volt self-winding spring-driven wall model with compensation mechanism for power interruption.

Three Mastercrafters (Chicago, Il) synchronous models. *Left,* Starlight. *Center,* swinging doll. *Right,* unusual model 209 simulating the action of the Jefferson models. (Right photo courtesy of Edward H. Voight)

Mercer Chronometer Corporation (England) ship's master clock to govern all common area clocks aboard ship. It was not involved with the ship's chronometer. *Left above,* front view of clock. *Left below,* "works" door open to show the movement in the case, the slave movement on the door and the advance/retard dials used to correct the time for different time zones. *Above,* bottom door opened to show remainder of mechanism.

Marlow and Co. (York, PA) miniature pillar and scroll powered by a Westinghouse motor.

Miller electric (USA) using Hatot patent ATO movement. *Left,* front view. *Right,* close-up of movement.

Reproduction Ben Franklin Clock made by Paragon Electric Company (Two Rivers, WI). This is believed to be the only consumer clock made by Paragon which manufactures timing devices and switches for both home an industrial use.

National Self-Winding Company (Champaign, IL striking mantle clock. *Upper,* front view. *Lower,* close-up of movement which has a mercury switch missing.

Synchronous Tymeter models made by Pennwood Numechron of Pittsburgh, PA (circa 1960). *Left and right above,* desk models. *Left,* "television" model. *Right,* bottom of television model showing Synchron motor on left and dial wheels.

Pul-syn-etic (England) master clock. *Left,* front view. *Above,* close-up of movement.

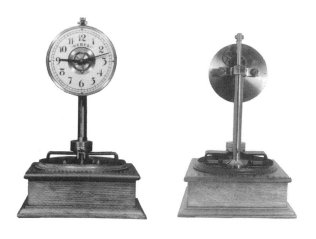

Rebesi globe model. *Left*, front view with dome removed. note the magnet on either side of the base. *Right*, rear view showing the relatively simple "works".

Sauter (Switzerland) astronomic type time switch which will turn lights on and off at differing times by season.

Synchronous desk clock made by Rex-Cole Co. (USA).

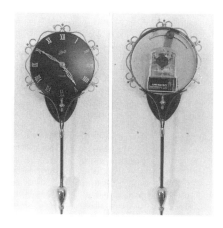

Recluse (France) dome model. *Left*, front view. *Right*, rear view showing movement.

Schatz (Germany) quartz novelty clock. The entire clock swings as a pendulum. *Left*, front view. *Right*, view of back showing the "swing" mechanism.

Very unusual triple waiting train movement clock by Solari (Italy), used in airports, train stations, etc. *Left*, front view. *Right*, rear view showing the mechanism which is powered by a Haddon motor.

Desk set made by Swift and Anderson (Boston, MA). Synchronous clock on the right and barometer on left.

Jeweled electric clock made by the South Bend Watch Co. (South Bend, IN). Few of these were ever manufactured. (Photo courtesy of Steve Cunningham)

Everhot appliance timers made by Schwartzbaugh (Toledo, OH)

Telephone Manufacturing Company (England) electrically restored weight-driven master clock following Princeps system and similar to Synchronome. Widely used in the English time system which was similar to the Western Union system in America, but had no correction feature. *Left*, front view. *Right*, close-up of movement.

Electrically restored weight-driven wall regulator by Alois Winbauer of Baden, Germany. The clock has a Riefler Type J pendulum and is 80-beat. (Photo courtesy of Don Brown)

Large program clock by an unknown maker. *Left,* front view. *Right,* doors open to show movement.

Electrically driven precision pendulum made to operate in a vacuum. maker unknown. *Left,* overall mechanism in it's housing. *Right,* close-up to show detail of contacts and pendulum.

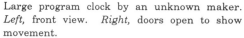

Massive mantle clock with an electrically wound spring-driven marine style movement, maker unknown. *Left,* front view. *Right,* view of movement removed from case.

◄ Powder box type tape measure clock similar to a Lux model, but by an unknown maker.

Whitehall-Hammond (USA) time only ► desk clock.

Windsor (USA) synchronous windmill clock.

United Metal Goods Manufacturing Co., Brooklyn, NY dancing doll model.

Novelty one-hand synchronous bird cage clock by unknown maker.

Woodbrook Enterprises, Inc. (Colorado Springs, Co) pillar clock which utilizes a compact disc player to reproduce the chimes of famous clocks, synchronized to their quartz movements.

Wagner (Germany) 220 volt electrically restored weight-driven movement.

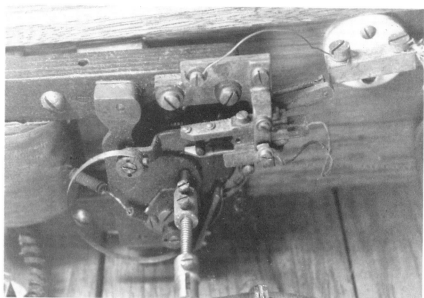

Aron System electrically rewound spring-driven movement. *Upper left*, view of movement showing the large heavy ring gear used in winding. *Above*, close-up of rewind motor and shaft which connects to the shaft above the ring gear in the photo at upper left. *Lower left*, view of the suspension. *Below*, name plate from movement.

ADDENDUM

We are indebted to Dr. P.T.M. Doensen of Utrecht, The Netherlands, for the material in this Addendum. Unfortunately, Dr. Doensen did not know of us, and this project, until we were well into page makeup on this work. This precluded the inclusion of the copy in the body of the text. Since we felt it to be of interest and value, however, it has been included here. We apologize for this and trust Dr. Doensen and our readers will understand.

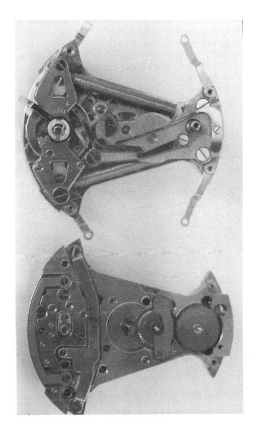

Lip (France) #1 movement balance wheel electric watch, the first electric watch in Europe and the first in the world to be patented. *Left*, back of case showing the back-set and openings for two batteries. *Center upper*, back view of movement showing coils and balance wheel. *Center lower*, dial side of movement. *Right*, dial view.

Diagram of the first Lip movement showing the two batteries (pile), the coils and the balance. ▶

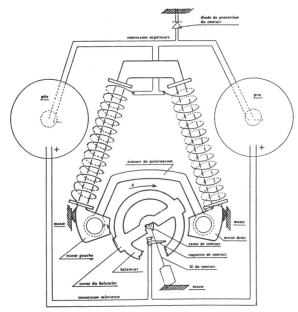

◀ Dauphine (France) electric wrist watch by Lip. *Left*, back removed to show Lip #2 one battery balance wheel movement. *Right*, dial view.

◀ Avia (Switzerland) electric balance wheel watch from Swiss Ebauches SA which utilizes a Maltese cross magnet mounted on the balance. According to the *Horological Journal*, these movements were used in a number of differently named watches such as Avia, Admes and Schild.

Zenith (Switzerland) tuning fork watch made under license ▶ from Bulova. This was the first tuning fork watch made in Europe.

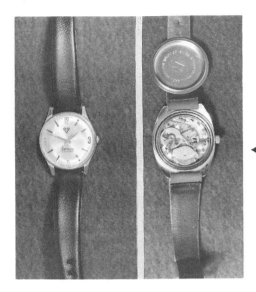

◀ Benrus electric balance wheel watch made in France.

Record (Switzerland) quartz-balance wheel watch with unusual time setting on the back of the case and date setting stem on the side. A rare watch. ▶

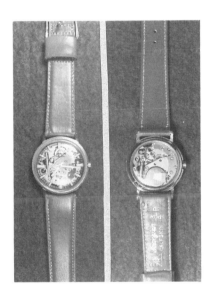

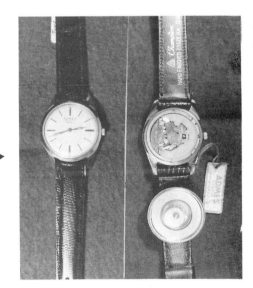

◀ Gotham crystal dial watch using a Lip #2 movement.

Admes (Switzerland) watch with Swiss Ebauches Maltese cross movement. ▶

Cross-sectional drawing of the Bulova Thermachron "body heat" watch pictured on page 18. Introduced into Europe in the early 19080's, the watch was designed to convert body heat to electric energy which powered the watch. A basically solid-state device senses the difference in temperature between the "cold" and "hot" parts of the watch and the tiny thermoelectric generator produces the power needed. The back of the case which is against the wearer's skin, the "hot" part of the case, is insulated from the rest of the case and detects the body heat through a special surface. The difference between this and the "cold" upper part of the case powers the generator which converts heat energy into electric energy. The voltage generated is then transformed through a sophisticated electronic circuit to the voltage needed to power the watch and can be stored in a rechargeable accumulator (a rechargeable battery? EDS.) A temperature change of as little as one degree was said to affect the watch and it was stated that the electric energy produced in a day was four to six times greater than that required to run the watch on a given day.

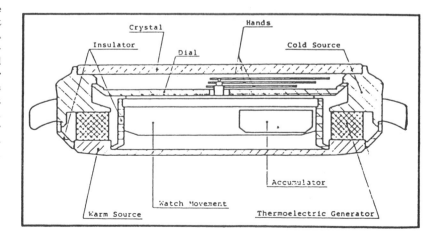